The Theoretical Significance
of
Experimental Relativity

Documents on Modern Physics

Edited by

ELLIOTT W. MONTROLL, Institute of Defense Analyses
GEORGE H. VINEYARD, Brookhaven National Laboratory

Additional volumes in preparation

The Theoretical Significance
of
Experimental Relativity

R. H. DICKE

Department of Physics,
Princeton University,
Princeton, New Jersey

GORDON AND BREACH
Science Publishers

New York • London

Library of Congress Catalog Card Number 64-25799

First Printing January 1965

Second Printing May 1965

These lectures were presented at the Les Houches Summer School of Theoretical Physics, and published in the proceedings volume, Relativity, Groups and Topology, C. De Witt et al, Eds., Gordon & Breach, 1964.

The author has corrected and amended the lectures for this edition.

Editorial Offices for Great Britain and Europe:
Gordon and Breach Science Publishers, Ltd.
171 Strand
London, W. C. 2, England

Distributed in the United Kingdom by:
Blackie & Son, Ltd.
5 Fitzhardinge Street
London, W. 1, England

Printed in the United States of America

EDITOR'S PREFACE

Seventy years ago when the fraternity of physicists was smaller than the audience at a weekly physics colloquium in a major university, a J. Willard Gibbs could, after ten years of thought, summarize his ideas on a subject in a few monumental papers or in a classic treatise. His competition did not intimidate him into a muddled correspondence with his favorite editor nor did it occur to his colleagues that their own progress was retarded by his leisurely publication schedule.

Today the dramatic phase of a new branch of physics spans less than a decade and subsides before the definitive treatise is published. Moreover, modern physics is an extremely interconnected discipline and the busy practitioner of one of its branches must be kept aware of breakthroughs in other areas. An expository literature which is clear and timely is needed to relieve him of the burden of wading through tentative and hastily written papers scattered in many journals.

To this end we have undertaken the editing of a new series, entitled *Documents on Modern Physics,* which will make available selected reviews, lecture notes, conference proceedings, and important collections of papers in branches of physics of special current interest. Complete coverage of a field will not be a primary aim. Rather, we will emphasize readability, speed of publication, and importance to students and research workers. The books will appear in low-cost paper-covered editions, as well as in cloth covers. The scope will be broad, the style informal.

From time to time, older branches of physics come alive again, and forgotten writings acquire relevance to recent developments. We expect to make a number of such works available by including them in this series along with new works.

ELLIOTT W. MONTROLL
GEORGE H. VINEYARD

PREFACE

This thin volume represents the notes, including a number of reprinted articles, for my course of lectures at the Les Houches summer school in July, 1963. The lectures were devoted to a discussion of a few key experiments and to their interpretation. Where so few experimental facts are available, one is driven to extract the maximum in theoretical interpretation, and these notes represent my attempt to both define and observationally delimit a class of relativistic theories of gravitation.

I consider it a privilege to have been able to spend two weeks in conversation and seminars with some of the best young theorists from both sides of the iron curtain, and as an experimentalist I attempted to counteract in some small measure the decided tendency in times past for General Relativity to develop into a formal science divorced from both observations and the rest of physics. A well known physicist once remarked to me that Einstein's General Relativity was such a beautiful theory that it was a shame that there were so few experiments. An examination of the scientific literature of the past 50 years will testify to the truth of this statement, the number of experimental papers being entirely negligible in comparison with the flood of theoretical publications, mostly formal.

Because of the great weakness of gravitation, results are far easier to obtain by calculation than by measurement. The experimentalist is unable to complement and guide the theorist in the manner that occurs in the other parts of physics. This elementary difficulty is a fact that the experimentalist must face, but the very lack of relativity experiments sharpens the challenge and increases the importance of the few experiments that are possible.

In my view, the grand opportunity for the experimentalist lies not in the applications of General Relativity but rather in its foundations. It would be a shame for dozens of very able theorists to devote a second half century to developing the results of General Relativity only to discover eventually that the theory is defective, that some basic assumption is incorrect.

In attempting to establish an observational basis for a relativistic theory of gravitation, I drew from the most important observations available in July 1963, including several new ones. However, the facts were so few that I was unwilling to pose the usual simple question, to ask if these few observations were compatible with General Relativity. I was curious to know how many other reasonable theories would also be supported by these same facts.

The observational results considered can be classified as follows:

    a) Null experiments of extreme precision.
    b) Null experiments of ordinary precision.
    c) The famous three tests of General Relativity.
    d) Cosmological observations.

Although all four types of experiments were covered in my lectures, in the two short weeks available I could not develop in my notes parts (c) and (d) to the extent that I would have liked. This is made up in part by several of the reprinted articles in the appendices.

In broadening the class of acceptable theories, I was unwilling to consider any but relativistic field theories. I considered it important to require general covariance and to permit only field theories derivable from an invariant action principle. The resulting very large class of theories, which includes General Relativity as special case, is explored in Appendix 4.

The reason for limiting the class of theories in this way is to be found in matters of philosophy, not in the observations. Foremost among these considerations was the philosophy of Bishop G. Berkeley and E. Mach.

It proved to be impossible to broaden the class of gravitational theories in this way without questioning two of the cardinal principles of General Relativity, the strong equivalence principle and the principle of a purely geometrical description of gravitation.

The strong equivalence principle is so sweeping in its implications that it reduces this large class of theories to a single example, that of Einstein. The situation regarding the geometrical interpretation is a bit more complicated. In the case of Einstein's theory, many definitions of a Riemannian geometry are possible but only one falls out in a natural way. If this definition is used, the gravitational field is described in purely geometrical terms, the field tensor being intrepreted as the metric tensor of the geometry. However, for every other theory in this very large class, the introduction of an operationally defined metric tensor is either impossible or else ambiguous, a large number of equally satisfactory definitions being possible.

Under these conditions it proved to be necessary to demote geometry from the central position that it occupies in Einstein's theory to a secondary position. Einstein's theory is not functionally damaged by this reinterpretation, although many would regard such a field theoretic interpretation as less elegant and beautiful than the geometrical one. There is probably room for disagreement on such questions of aesthetics; in any case their importance for physics can be questioned.

It is interesting to note that although this class of possible relativistic field theories of gravitation is enormous, the experiments discussed in the notes make unlikely any but a very limited sub-class, containing only Einstein's theory and the various theories requiring both tensor and scalar zero mass fields. This interpretation of the observations is discussed in the main body of the notes as well as in Appendix 4.

Owing to the short period in which they were written, the notes are uneven, certain sections receiving an adequate treatment but other equally important parts being almost completely ignored. Perhaps the most serious lack is a discussion of Mach's principle, for the philosophy of Berkeley and Mach always lurked in the background and influenced all of my thoughts.

During our two week stay at Les Houches Mach's principle was frequently under discussion. Upon our arrival at Les Houches on a Sunday evening, my daughter, Nancy, and I were welcomed by Bryce DeWitt with the invitation to join a Mach's Principle Seminar scheduled to start in a few minutes. This was the second of a series of some half dozen exciting and at times contentious seminars on the subject. Above all else, these seminars conducted by F. Karoly-hazy, F. Gürsey, J. A. Wheeler and me showed that there was no general agreement on the meaning, significance or importance of this principle for physics. However, my own thinking in recent years has been strongly conditioned by this philosophy.

As mentioned above, the philosophy of Berkeley and Mach furnished the philosophical framework for the class of theories described in Appendix 4. The physical picture is one of a 4-dimensional world populated by structureless particles. These particles are not only the real and virtual particles of laboratory physics, but also the zero mass bosons, mostly virtual, assumed to be responsible for gravitational and inertial forces. Contrary to the philosophy of Newton but consistent with Mach's viewpoint, inertial forces are pictured in Appendix 4 as "real" being acceleration dependent forces having their origin in collisions with gravitons, particles associated with a symmetric tensor field.

As of this writing we seem to be very far from a situation requiring gravitons and the quantization of the gravitational field, therefore it is helpful to remember that boson fields do not exhibit important quantum fluctuation effects when they are strong and contain only low frequency components. While in our speculations we may have pictured a space populated with a host of gravitons, it seemed reasonable to develop a theory of *classical* boson fields interacting with *classical* particles. It seemed certain that almost all the interesting gravitational physics could be encompassed in such a non-quantized treatment of the gravitational field or fields. The gravitational interaction is viewed as basically not different from other interactions, and that the treatment as a classical unquantized field should be regarded as a good approximation to a proper quantized treatment.

The empty physical space I picture as a void without properties, the physical properties of the space, when populated, arising wholly from its material content. As emphasized by Bishop Berkeley, the motion of a single test particle in such an otherwise empty space is a meaningless physical concept; but populate this space with particles and the motion can be given meaning through the altered pattern of collisions with the particles filling the space, a geometrical point being identified with a space-time coincidence of two particles. Alternatively, when quantum fluctuations are beyond our vision, a set of invariants derived from the various massless boson fields might be used to help identify a geometrical point.

Mach's ideas about the nature of inertial forces were the anti-thesis of the philosophy of Newton and Locke. From our first contact with physics we have been exposed to Newton's philosophy. We all learned that forces were the pushes or pulls which one body exerted upon another, and that the forces acting upon a body were to be summed, divided by the mass of the particle, and equated to the acceleration of the body. The acceleration was to be pictured as *caused* by this force. When we studied Einstein's relativity, both Special and General, we again encountered this essentially Newtonian idea but expressed in a four dimensional form.

As pointed out already in 1710 by Bishop Berkeley, and later elaborated by E. Mach, the Newtonian scheme has logical difficulties. The acceleration is to be reckoned with respect to "absolute space", a concept emphasized by Berkeley to be without an observational basis. What one actually measures is always an acceleration relative to other, generally distant matter in the universe.

As emphasized by Mach, with this interpretation of the acceleration there is no longer a clear distinction between the "real" (eg. electrical and nuclear) forces and "illusionary" (inertial) forces of physics. While Mach's writings are difficult to interpret, it appears to have been his view that inertial forces were action-at-a-distance acceleration dependent forces produced by interactions with the distant matter of the universe. He interpreted such inertial forces as just as real as other action-at-a-distance forces such as electromagnetism or gravitation.

To give a modern interpretation to Mach's ideas it is necessary to interpret inertial forces as acceleration dependent interactions of a particle with a field generated by the distant matter in the universe. Using the standard machinery of Lorentz invariant field theory, it is easy to show the forces generated by a symmetric tensor field interacting with a particle are of two types, being velocity and acceleration dependent. However, as shown by W. Thirring, the introduction of such a tensor field destroys the observability and physical significance of the Minkowski metric tensor of special relativity. The interaction of a tensor field with matter so distorts meter sticks and clocks that they no longer measure the Euclidean geometry of special relativity.

In Appendix 4 the Newtonian philosophy is abandoned; relativistic field theory is developed without the introduction of either a metric or affine connection. The arbitrarily chosen coordinate system is to be interpreted only as a convenient labeling of an almost continuous pattern of collisions between the particles filling the space. The physical concepts of distance, curvature, or geodesic path are to be avoided until the dynamical problems are solved. After the equations of motion are obtained, for certain combinations of zero-mass boson fields it is useful to introduce a definition of the metric of a Riemannian geometry. For other combinations, a physically meaningful definition is impossible.

Palmer Physical Laboratory
Princeton University
February 4, 1964

CONTENTS

Introduction

Before discussing in detail the present status of experimental work on gravitation, it is necessary to consider briefly the unique problems and opportunities faced by the experimentalist working in this field. Experiments seems to play quite different roles, and to present very different problems, in the various fields of physics. For example, in high energy physics the experimenter is the explorer, new particles are still being discovered, and even the qualitative aspects of their interactions are not yet completely understood. In this field there is not yet a satisfactory theory and the experiments are essential for the construction of a theory.

On the other hand, in solid state physics the basic physical laws are well known, for the electromagnetic interaction of electrons and nuclei with each other is well understood in its broader aspects. It is only the complications of the many body problem that prohibits a complete theoretical treatment of solid state physics. Experiments in this branch of physics provide insight into the complications of the many body problem.

The problems of the experimentalist working on gravitation differ from both of the above. Here there is an elegant, well defined theory but almost no experiments. The situation is almost orthogonal to that in both high energy physics and solid state physics. Far from experimental science being a crutch on which the theory leans, in the case of general relativity, theory has far outstripped experiment, and the big problem is one of finding significant experiments to perform. This situation raises serious problems for theory and our understanding of gravitation. For where there are no experiments the theory easily degenerates into purely formal mathematics.

At this stage it might be asked whether either experiment or theory in this field is important to the rest of physics. Certainly it was the prevailing attitude during the thirties and forties that general relativity was of little importance to a physicist. This was caused by an apparent lack of connection with laboratory science. In fact, a slightly naïve application of the equivalence principle seems at first glance to force this point of view. If gravitation is transformed away locally (i.e., a coordinate frame, locally inertial, is chosen), then externally produced gravitational effects apparently disappear in the laboratory. From this it is a short step to conclude that the external universe is without effect on the laboratory and that cosmology is of no concern to the physicist.

But certainly this is too provincial a point of view. The physicist cannot limit his horizon to the narrow confines of his little laboratory. Whether he likes it or not he is in the universe. His apparatus is made of cosmological stuff, and he should be curious about its origins. The walls of his laboratory are penetrated by neutrinos, probably by gravitons, and possibly by scalarons generated by the distant matter in the universe in ancient times. Also, the structure of the elementary particles, his stock and trade, may be dominated at small distances by gravitational effects.

In other fields of physics the experimentalist is faced with the problem of choosing the most important out of a large number of possible experiments. With gravitation the problem is different. There are so few possible experiments, and their importance is such, that any and all significant experiments should be performed. As an example, it can be argued that the gravitational red shift is a result to be expected from little more than energy considerations (see later discussion) and is not a significant test of general relativity. While to some extent this is true, I feel that an experiment such as this is worth while, as it adds to the general body of knowledge and reduces the area of conjecture.

While all relativity experiments are important, in my view the most important are the highly precise null experiments to be discussed. These, carefully interpreted, provide a substantial observational foundation for certain parts of the structure of general relativity and also show where information is lacking. Second most important are the so-called fundamental tests of general relativity, such as the relativistic perihelion rotation of planetary orbits. While these do not have the precision that one would like, they provide valuable insight into the form of the field, or fields, associated with the central force problem. The third part, which could be easily rocketed into first place of importance by a significant discovery, is the general area of cosmological effects. These concern a wide variety of subjects: possible gravitational or scalar waves from space, the effects of a quasi-static scalar field generated by distant matter (if such a field exists), the continuous creation cosmology (which should be either laid to rest or else cured of its ills), Schwarzschild stars if they exist (a Schwarzschild star is one for which the star's matter is falling down the gullet of the Schwarzschild solution), massive generators of gravitational radiation, the global aspects of the structure of the universe, and the origin of matter. All these and many more are subjects concerning effects on a cosmological scale. These effects, if they could be observed, would give information about the most fundamental of the problems of physics.

It is worth asking why experimental work on gravitation is so different and has such a different status from experiments in other fields. This is probably due to the extreme weakness of the gravitational interaction, only 10^{-40} of the strength of the strong interactions. Because of this great weakness, an experimentalist is forced to modify his conceptions of what an experimentalist is and does. Traditionally an experimental physicist has been able to isolate a problem in the laboratory and to devise controlled experiments designed to look at one aspect of his complex problem. He has made real progress by concetrating on one specific thing. However, because of the great weakness of gravitation, the experimentalist working on gravitation might like to perform experiments on an astronomical scale. For example, he might like to take two bodies of 10^{33} gm mass and a density of 10^6 gm per cubic centimeter and whirl them about each other at high speed. He clearly cannot do this in the laboratory, but he may find nature performing just such an experiment for him if he looks hard enough.

Experiment and observation can become intertwined in this field of physics, and will probably become more so in the future. The chief difference between the experimental physicist trying to get information from observations on the galaxy and the astrophysicist doing the same, is that the physicist, working on a particular gravitational problem, is considering the astrophysical observations for a specific physical reason. He is not concerned with galactic structure *per se* but views the whole galaxy as a giant laboratory in which many millions of experiments are being carried out simultaneously on an enormous scale. The physicist may want to look around carefully among this enormous number of colossal "experiments" to see if by some fluke one of them is just the one that he would have liked to perform in the laboratory himself. While his chance of finding exactly the experimental setup that he would have liked is rather small, there may be many of these "experiments" that have some bearing on his particular problem.

In the cosmological field, the ground under foot, the interior of the earth, element abundances, and the form of the solar system are all capable of providing important clues to the answer of important physical questions. Here there is no paucity of relativity experiments to perform; rather the problem is one of interpretation. Almost invariably the astrophysical and geophysical systems are so complex that a simple, clear, and unambiguous answer to a straightforward physical question cannot be obtained. However, a limited answer has some validity, for it can contribute slightly to a gradually evolving picture of the physical situation. Each fact by itself may have only a very small importance, but taken all together these facts can constitute an important part of our total knowledge.

I. Null Experiments

Eötvös Experiment

Of the various null experiments, perhaps the most important is the Eötvös experiment, first performed in 1889 by Baron Roland v. Eötvös and recently repeated by the author's research group. This experiment showed with great precision that all bodies fall with the same acceleration. Actually the roots of this experiment go back much farther than this. Newton, and many others after him, demonstrated experimentally that the gravitational acceleration of a body was independent of its composition. Even the ancient Greeks must have had some ideas along this line, and it seems likely that the famous theoretical proof of Aristotle that the gravitational acceleration of a heavy body was very much greater than that of a light body must have flown in the face of the everyday observations of the Greek world. It seems likely that, long before the Greeks, primitive man must have observed that a lizard knocked out of a tree by a stone fell to the ground almost simultaneously with the stone.

The importance of the Eötvös experiment rests primarily upon the fact that the null result of this experiment is a *necessary* condition to be satisfied if Einstein's general relativity is to be valid. The geodesic motion of a structureless and spinless particle is a result of general relativity. The unique character of the trajectory is an elementary result which can even be derived directly from the equivalence principle. For small laboratory sized objects, accelerated in the gravitational field of the sun or earth, the effect of finite size or of spin angular momentum on the trajectory is negligible, and to a good approximation geodesic motion would be expected.

In the experiment performed by the Princeton group, the gravitational acceleration toward the sun of small gold and aluminum weights were compared and found to be equal with an accuracy of about a part in 10^{11}. Hence, the *necessary* condition to be satisfied seems to be rather satisfactorily met. Perhaps a more interesting question is this: To what extent is this experiment also a *sufficient* condition to be satisfied in order that general relativity be valid?

Before discussing this, it is important to note that gold and aluminum differ from each other rather greatly in several important ways. First, the neutron to proton ratio is quite different in the two elements, varying from 1·08 in aluminum to 1·5 in gold. Second, the electrons in aluminum move with non-relativistic velocities, but in gold the k-shell electrons have a 15 per cent increase in their mass as a result of their relativistic velocities. Third, the electromagnetic negative contribution to the binding energy of the nucleus varies as Z^2 and represents $\frac{1}{2}$ per cent of the total mass of a gold atom, whereas it is negligible in aluminum. In similar fashion, the virtual pair field around the gold nucleus would be expected to represent a far bigger contribution to the total energy than in the case of aluminum. Also the virtual pion field, and other virtual fields, would be expected to be different in the two atoms. We would conclude that in most physical aspects gold and aluminum differ substantially from each other and that the equality of their accelerations represents a very important condition to be satisfied by any theory of gravitation.

It should be remarked that no experiment can provide a *sufficient* condition for a theory to be valid, as all experiments have only a finite accuracy. But the accuracy of the Eötvös experiment is very great. Does this imply that the equivalence principle is very nearly valid? It will be shown that this is only true in a limited sense. Certain aspects of the equivalence principle are not supported in the slightest by the Eötvös experiment.

In order to understand the limited conclusions to be drawn from the Eötvös experiment, we must first consider the significance of the equivalence principle for relativity. In this connection it may be convenient to make a distinction between the strong equivalence principle upon which Einstein's general relativity is based and the weak equivalence principle supported by the Eötvös experiment. The strong equivalence principle might be defined as the assumption that in a freely falling, non-rotating, laboratory the local laws of physics take on some standard form, including a standard numerical content, independent of the position of the laboratory in space and time. It is of course implicit in this statement that the effects of gradients in the gravitational field strength are negligibly small, i.e., tidal interaction effects are negligible. The weak principle of equivalence says considerably less; it states only that the local gravitational acceleration is substantially independent of the composition and structure of the matter being accelerated.

The significance of the strong form of the principle of equivalence for relativity appears to be the following: This principle requires that the laws of physics, expressed in a coordinate system, locally inertial, shall take on some standard form and have some standard numerical content. As a laboratory, neither rotating nor accelerating, in gravity free space provides a particular example of the situation described above. the assumption that physical laws are correctly described in gravity free space by the usual Lorentz-invariant formalism implies that for the more general situation, where gravitation is present, the formalism should reduce locally to this standard Lorentz invariant form (with local Minkowski coordinate conditions).

It is well known that this interpretation of the equivalence principle, plus the assumption of general covariance is most of what is needed to generate Einstein's general relativity.

The numerical content of the locally observed laws of physics is contained in the dimensionless physical constants appearing in the formulation of physical laws. These include the ratios of the masses of elementary particles, the various coupling constants of the theory, such as the fine structure constant, and the ratios of the masses of elementary particles to the characteristic fundamental gravitational mass $(\hbar c/G)^{1/2}$. Thus, one of the assumptions of the strong equivalence principle is that these dimensionless "constants" are truly constant, i.e., coordinate independent.

It is evident that the weak principle of equivalence is supported directly and strongly by the Eötvös experiment. But does it also support the strong principle? As will be shown, the answer is a limited yes. An argument, due originally to Wapstra and Nijgh[1], and only a slight elaboration of a familiar derivation of the gravitational red shift formula, can be used to sustain in part the strong principle.

Before discussing the argument we shall consider briefly this derivation of the gravitational red shift. The red shift can be obtained from the null result of the Eötvös experiment, mass energy equivalence, and the conservation of energy in a static gravitational field and static coordinate system. With the assumption that the inertial mass of a body is given by its total energy, the Eötvös experiment shows with considerable accuracy that the passive gravitational mass, or weight, is proportional to the inertial mass, hence to the energy of the body. Now consider an atom with two internal energy states and consider an energy reservoir, both to be placed initially on the floor of the laboratory. Let the atom, originally in the ground state, be excited by withdrawing energy from the reservoir. Then let it be lifted to the ceiling in its excited state. Let a photon be emitted and the atom lowered in its ground state to its original position on the floor. If the photon is caught in the energy reservoir and all the energy, positive and negative, used in lifting and lowering the atom be then gathered up in the reservoir, the assumption that this total energy is conserved is sufficient to give the correct result for the red shift. The proof is elementary. Assuming mass-energy equivalence and the null result of the Eötvös experiment, the weight of a body is equal to its internal energy multiplied by the local gravitational acceleration g. The total work required to lift it an infinitesimal distance dx in the excited state and lower it in its ground state is

$$dw = gEdx \tag{1}$$

where E is the excitation energy. For energy conservation to hold, the energy of the photon trapped in the energy reservoir must exceed the original photon energy withdrawn by

$$dE = gEdx. \tag{2}$$

It should be noted that except for the null result of the Eötvös experiment this result depends only upon the assumptions of mass-energy equivalence and energy

7*

conservation. For this reason the gravitational red shift experiment is not a very strong test of general relativity. We shall return to this point later when the so-called three fundamental tests of general relativity are discussed.

Now let us consider the implication of the Eötvös experiment for the constancy of the dimensionless physical constants, hence for the strong equivalence principle. This is best discussed with an example. Consider the question of whether the fine structure "constant" is really constant, hence independent of position. If we again make the assumptions of energy conservation and mass energy equivalence, the above argument can be used to show that the fine structure constant could not vary appreciably with position.

In order to show this, let us first assume the contrary. Then the internal energy of the atom is a function of position, this for a variety of reasons. For example, the electrostatic self energy of the nucleus is proportional to $z(z - 1)\alpha$. Also the electronic contribution to the total energy of an atom is approximately proportional to the square of the fine structure constant.

Once again assume a closed cycle in which the atom is first slowly lifted, this time in its ground state. In the raised position the atom is taken apart, being broken down either into elementary particles or into two or more atoms of smaller mass. These fragments are then gently lowered to the ground floor and reassembled into the original atom. Now it is easily seen that if the internal energy of the primary atom is a function of height, but not that of the fragments, the atom has an additional (anomalous) weight equal to the negative gradient of its internal energy. This is a necessary requirement for energy conservation. More generally, if the energies of the fragments are also variable, but by different amounts, the anomalous forces will be different for the fragments. It should be emphasized that only energy conservation is required to exhibit these anomalous forces.

Now with the additional assumption that the inertial masses of the atoms and elementary particles are equal to their internal energies, anomalous gravitational accelerations must appear, contrary to the null result of the Eötvös experiment. The expected anomalous acceleration is equal to

$$\delta a = -\frac{1}{m}\nabla m \quad (c = 1) \tag{3}$$

The strongest test of the constancy of the fine structure "constant" is provided not by the electronic contribution to the energy of the atom, but by the electrostatic contribution to the binding energy of the nucleus.* Here the equality of the gravitational acceleration toward the sun of aluminum and gold, to an accuracy of a part in 10^{11}, implies that the fine structure constant could vary with position relative to the sun by only an extremely minute amount. The fractional gradient of the fine structure constant due to the presence of the sun, could not exceed 5×10^{-31}/centimeter, or else the gravitational acceleration of gold relative to the sun would differ by more than a part in 10^{11} from that of aluminum. This is a very severe limit to the constancy of the fine structure constant, for one might expect that if there were a

---

* We do not consider separately the effect of electromagnetic contributions to the self energy of the elementary particles.

cosmological effect leading to a variation of the fine structure constant, the effect of the sun's presence would be of the order of [2,3]

$$\delta\alpha \sim -\alpha^2 \frac{GM}{rc^2} \tag{4}$$

where $\delta\alpha$ is the change in the fine structure constant due to the presence of the sun, and M and r are the mass of and distance to the sun. If there were a variation in the fine structure constant as large as that given by equation (4), there would be an anomalous gravitational acceleration 5×10^6 times as large as the limit set by the Eötvös experiment.

It must be emphasized that this conclusion depends on the assumption of the equivalence of inertial mass and energy, and the assumption of energy conservation. The close connection between time displacement invariance and energy conservation would appear to require the energy conservation principle for a static gravitational field described in a static coordinate system. However, the assumption of mass-energy equivalence is not quite so compelling. As will be discussed more in detail in the next section, the interaction of a particle with a second massless tensor field would generally lead to an anomaly in its inertial mass. However, the second null experiment to be described makes the existence of more than one long range tensor field unlikely. Consequently, the equivalence of the inertial mass of a body and its energy is assumed here. It is believed, therefore, that Wapstra's argument for the constancy of physical "constants" is valid. However, to avoid any misconceptions it should be remarked here that this constitutes a compelling argument for the constancy of only some of the physical constants. Before discussing this point in some detail we first consider a closely related problem.

In recent years it has frequently been suggested that the gravitational pull on an antiparticle might be negative. This suggestion ignores the fact that this is incompatible with the requirements of general relativity. (Consider, for example, the implications for the laws of gravitation of energy confined to a small perfectly reflecting box, being converted back and forth from a pair state to a photon state. If the positron coupling were negative, the gravitational field generated by the box would decrease while in the pair state.)

Schiff[4] has shown that an argument based on the Eötvös experiment and the standard Lorentz invariant laws governing laboratory physics can be used to exclude this possibility. The argument is simple. In the virtual photon field of the nucleus there exists also a virtual pair field derived from the photon field. If the positrons in this pair field were to tend to fall, up not down, there would be an anomalous weight of the atom, substantially greater for large atomic number than small. It is concluded because of the null result of the Eötvös experiment that positrons and other antiparticles fall down, not up.

What then can be concluded from the Eötvös experiment about the constancy of the physical "constants"? The conclusion seems to be that all the dimensionless physical constants differing no more than a few powers of 10 from unity are constant or are very nearly constant.

There are two physical constants, differing from unity by many powers of 10, for which this argument is without validity. These are the fantastically small Fermi and gravitational coupling constants. They have values respectively of approximately 10^{-13} for the Fermi constant and 10^{-40} for the gravitational coupling constant. The gravitational and Fermi interactions are so weak that the resulting contribution to the self energies of the atom are negligible; consequently they have no important effects upon the gravitational acceleration and the Eötvös experiment. An alternative way of expressing the possible variation of a gravitational coupling constant is to remark that the gravitational mass $(\hbar c/G)^{1/2} = 2.2 \times 10^{-5}$ gm may vary with respect to the masses of the elementary particles, or completely equivalently that the elementary particle masses may vary when compared with the gravitational mass. As will be discussed later the elementary particle masses would be expected to vary if these particles coupled with some long range, i.e., zero mass, scalar field.

If it some day should be shown that elementary particle masses were dependent upon such a field, this would be of considerable significance, for a scalar field, generated by the whole universe, would carry into the laboratory an effect dependent upon the structure of the whole universe. A physicist could hardly ignore cosmology if β decay rates and gravitational interaction strengths were to be dependent upon the dimension of the universe.

The above discussion has served to highlight the significance of the Eötvös experiment for relativity. Not only is the weak principle of equivalence supported directly and strongly by this experiment, but except for the question of the invariance of the gravitational and Fermi interaction strengths, the strong principle is also.

The Princeton Experiment. The early experimental work on the composition independence of the gravitational acceleration used pendulums. It was determined that, with considerable accuracy, the period of a pendulum was independent of the composition of the pendulum bob. This approach to the problem, using a pendulum, is apparently limited by the accuracy with which the period of the pendulum can be measured and also by the various effects disturbing the oscillation of the pendulum. Eötvös experiment differed in one important way from the earlier ones. His was a null experiment, i.e., he employed a static torsion balance, balancing a component of the earth's gravitational pull on a weight against the centrifugal force field of the earth acting on the weight. (While a centrifugal force field is an anathema to a teacher of elementary physics, in relativity it may be considered as an honest force, merely an aspect of the overall gravitational force field.)

In his torsion balance experiment, Eötvös employed a horizontal torsion beam, 40 cm long, suspended by a fine wire. From the ends of the torsion beam were suspended, one lower than the other, two masses of different composition. A lack of strict proportionality between the inertial and gravitational masses of the two bodies would lead to a torque tending to rotate the balance. In Eötvös apparatus there seems to be no good reason for the one mass being suspended lower than the other.

This experiment, first published in 1890 and later repeated, being published in 1922,[5] showed with an accuracy of a few parts in 10^9 that inertial and gravitational masses were equivalent. This was quite an achievement considering the time at which the experiment was done, and the techniques available at that time. With our more modern techniques we were only able to improve his results by $2\frac{1}{2}$ orders of magnitude.

The Princeton experiment, performed by P. G. Roll, R. Krotkov, and R. H. Dicke, was designed with the following points in mind:

(a) We wanted to use the acceleration toward the sun, rather than the centripetal acceleration due to earth's rotation, as the source of the inertial field. While the acceleration toward the sun is somewhat smaller, this deficiency is more than compensated for by the advantages of a controlled experiment. A great difficulty with using the earth's rotation as the source of the inertial force field is that it cannot be turned off. However, to explain the matter in egocentric terms, the sun moves around the earth every 24 hours, and any gravitational-inertial anomalies should appear with a 24-hour period rather than statically as in the case of the earth's centrifugal force field.

(b) Because of its large quadrupole moment, Eötvös' balance was quite sensitive to gradients in the gravitational field produced by nearby massive bodies, such as Baron Eötvös himself. To reduce difficulties of this type we used a three-fold symmetry axis in the torsion balance. This employed one gold weight and two aluminum weights at the three corners of a horizontal equilateral triangle. The dimensions of the triangle were kept small, only 6 centimeters on the side. Also the rotation of the torsion balance was observed remotely to eliminate gravitational disturbances produced by the observer.

(c) To eliminate disturbances produced by convective currents in the air a good vacuum was employed in the chamber containing the torsion balance. Also to reduce the air pressure gradient effects produced by thermal gradients in the apparatus, a good vacuum (10^{-8} mm) was used, and precautions were taken to hold temperature variations and gradients to very small values. The very low gas pressure also incidently greatly reduced the pressure fluctuation disturbances of the pendulum (i.e., Brownian motion effects), but this Brownian motion disturbance was usually unimportant when compared with the other disturbances, chiefly seismic in origin.

(d) As a means of controlling the temperature fluctuation and gradients, and of reducing ground disturbances, the instrument was located in a specially built remote instrument well 12 feet deep. This well was capped by a thermal insulating plug 4 feet thick. The instrument was operated remotely for months at a time without opening the well.

(e) To substantially eliminate the disturbances associated with the gradual creep of the suspension wire, it was replaced by a fused quartz fibre, coated with a thin film of aluminum.

(f) To eliminate the highly undesirable dynamical characteristics of an underdamped torsion balance, the rotation of the balance was sensed remotely and the resulting error signal fed back through a corrector network as a torque on the balance. This served not only to dampen the balance but to decrease its period.

(g) The balance was designed and built to eliminate magnetic contamination, as the fluctuations in the earth's magnetic field could otherwise lead to inordinately large disturbances of the balance.

(h) Insulating surfaces which could have become electrostatically charged were eliminated from the balance.

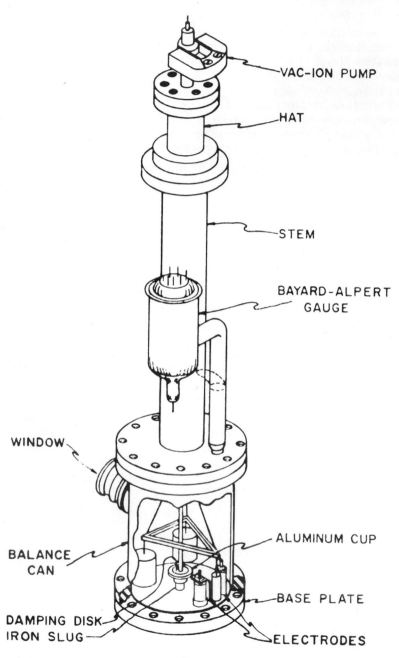

VAC-ION PUMP

HAT

STEM

BAYARD-ALPERT
GAUGE

WINDOW

BALANCE
CAN

ALUMINUM CUP

BASE PLATE

DAMPING DISK
IRON SLUG

ELECTRODES

Fig. 1

(i) The data were recorded continuously and automatically and analyzed statistically on an electronic computer.

(j) A number of temperature and temperature gradient measurements could be made in the well remotely. Two of the temperatures were continuously recorded.

A schematic view of the torsion balance is shown in Fig. 1. Note the smaller gold weight between the two copper electrodes used to apply feed back torques to the balance.

The basic features of the principles of operation are easily seen by considering the situation at 6:00 a.m. with the apparatus so oriented that the mirror faces south, i.e., the gold weight is toward the north. It is evident that the gravitational pull of the sun on the gold weight tends to rotate the balance clockwise but that this is balanced by the inertial reaction force in the coordinate system in which the apparatus is stationary. A similar balance exists for the two aluminum weights. If the balance should not be exactly the same for aluminum and gold, a small excess force would act on the aluminum or gold causing the balance to tend to rotate. Assume for purposes of discussion that the gold weight should accelerate toward the sun slightly more than the aluminum. Then the balance would tend to rotate clockwise. At 6:00 p.m. the situation is reversed and the rotation should be reversed. Thus not only is a 24-hour period required for a significant effect, but the phase must be correct. As a test on any observed 24-hour effect, the whole apparatus could be rotated through 90°, 180°, or 270°, and a new set of observations taken.

It is necessary to say a few words about the necessity for electronic damping of the balance. With a completely linear device this should not have been necessary, as the response of the balance to disturbances at its resonance frequency ($0 \cdot 00243$ sec^{-1}) is irrelevant. Its response at a frequency of 24^{-1} hr.$^{-1}$ is all that matters to the experiment. Actually because of non-linear effects, such damping is very important. When any vibration mode of the balance is strongly excited, second order effects start to appear, and these effects tend to change the effective zero of the apparatus. As these excitations will change with time, the effect on the zero is an unpredictable fluctuation and is a severe limit to the accuracy of the experiment. It is consequently necessary to keep all the normal modes of the pendulum from being strongly excited. In the case of the torsion mode the problem is particularly severe, as the frequency of this oscillation is so low that any disturbance of the rotation of the pendulum is apt to last a very long time without damping. If one were to assume a Q of the suspension fiber of 10^5, a strong excitation of oscillation of the torsion mode would persist for 2 years. Thus any strong disturbance, localized in time, such as an earthquake, blasting, etc., would strongly disturb the pendulum, and this disturbance would not disappear for a long time.

In similar fashion the swinging mode of the pendulum, various rocking modes, as well as the fiber stretching vibrational mode, when strongly excited would give a spurious deflection to the torsion balance. This was particularly apparent after an earthquake or other seismic disturbance. Fortunately the Q's of these higher frequency modes were not so high as to lead to very long damping times, hence objectionable troubles. The torsion mode electrical damping shortened the damping time of this mode sufficiently that there was also no trouble from this cause.

It was important to be able to detect an extremely small rotation of the torsion balance ($\sim 10^{-9}$ rad.) without disturbing the balance. This was accomplished by a

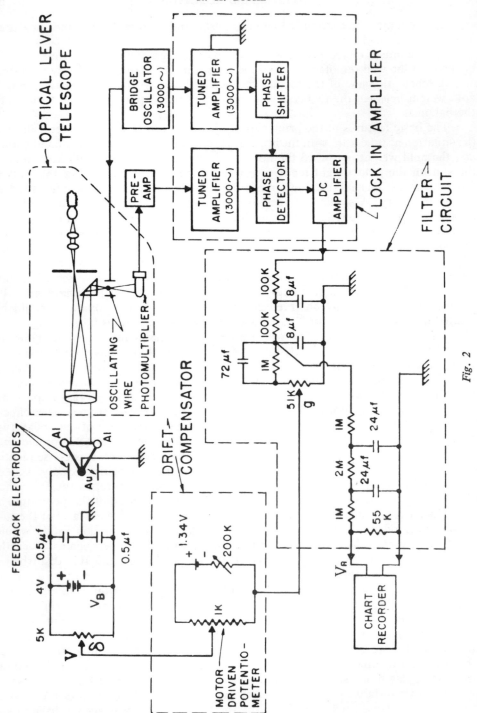

Fig. 2

very weak light beam reflected from the mirror. The apparatus used is shown schematically in Fig. 2. Light from a narrow slit is collimated by a telescope objective, reflected from the optical flat polished on one face of the quartz triangle of the torsion balance, a mirror (0·25 cm × 5·5 cm), and reflected back through the objective to form a real image. This image is caused to fall upon a wire of about the same width as the slit image. The light transmitted by the wire falls upon a photo multiplier. The wire is caused to oscillate back and forth across the slit image. If the image is centered perfectly only even harmonics of the oscillation frequency appear. However, if the image is displaced slightly to one side, the fundamenal frequency appears in the light intensity. By multiplying the output voltage of the photo multiplier by the fundamental modulation frequency of the wire, a D.C. voltage is developed whenever the fundamental frequency is present in the light output. Its magnitude and sign depend upon the amount and direction of the displacement of the slit image relative to the wire. This voltage after suitable filtering is applied to the electrical system as shown in Fig. 2 to restore the pendulum to its zero position. The voltage necessary to restore the pendulum to its zero position is recorded as a measure of the torque acting on the balance.

Table I gives the chief results of this series of measurements.

It is concluded that aluminum and gold fall toward the sun with the same acceleration, the accelerations differing from each other by at most 1 part in 10^{11}.

TABLE I

Principal results of the torsion balance measurements of the difference in passive gravitational-to-inertial mass ratios.

Balance A	Weights B	Direction of Telescope	Number of Runs N	Mean value of $\eta(A, B)$[a]
Gold	Aluminum	North	20	[b] $(2·2 \pm 1·4) \times 10^{-11}$
		South	18	$(0·4 \pm 1·5) \times 10^{-11}$
		North + South	38	$(0·96 \pm 1·04) \times 10^{-11}$
Copper	PbCl$_2$ + pyrex flask	————	5	[c] $(0 \pm 1·4) \times 10^{-10}$

[a] $$\eta(A, B) . \equiv . \frac{(M^A/m^A) - (M_B/m_B)}{\frac{1}{2}[(M^A/m^A) + (M_B/m_B)]},$$

where M represents passive gravitational mass and m represents inertial mass.

[b] The results quoted for the gold-aluminum torsion balance are the means of N measurements $\pm$ the probable error of the corresponding means.

[c] The results quoted for the copper—PbCl$_2$ torsion balance represent the root mean square noise level at a frequency of (1/24 hr), averaged for the five data runs made. The five runs were made with three different orientations of the telescope, and in no case was the 24-hr fourier amplitude observed to exceed the general noise level in the frequency range near (1/24 hr).

Space Isotropies

The next null experiment requiring discussion is that on spatial isotropy performed by Hughes, Robinson and Beltran–Lopez[6], and independently by Drever[7]. This experiment has an interesting history. Devised as a test of Mach's principle, in accordance with the suggestion of Cocconi and Salpeter[8], in the opinion of the author[9] it has little to say about this principle directly, but it is equally important for another reason. It is important, as it constitutes an extremely severe test of the local isotropy of space and this imposes a strong condition on any theory of gravitation. To state the matter more carefully, any zero mass Boson field is capable of yielding quasi-static interactions between matter. However, the tremendous precision of the Hughes–Drever experiment sets precise conditions on these fields namely, they must be such as to permit a choice of coordinate system for which physical laws appear locally and spacially, isotropic.

It is important to remember that it is a property of general relativity that a coordinate system may always be chosen to be locally Minkowskian. For this choice of coordinate system, in the absence of an externally produced electromagnetic field and with the assumption that second derivatives of the metric tensor are sufficiently small, the laws of physics are spacially isotropic, i.e., invariant under arbitrary rotations of the whole laboratory relative to this space. However, inasmuch as the result of any experiment is an invariant, depending only upon the relation of the apparatus to the measured system, the fact that isotropy exists in one coordinate system is sufficient to show that for any coordinate system, phenomena observed in the laboratory should be independent of the orientation of the laboratory relative to the distant matter of the universe.

In the Hughes–Drever experiment to be described, because of the earth's rotation, the orientation of the laboratory changes with time. An extremely sensitive test of possible effects of this change in orientation is devised.

It is clear from the above that the null result of the Hughes–Drever experiment constitutes a severe *necessary* condition to be satisfied, but this does not imply that this is the only relativistic theory of gravitation compatible with the condition of local isotropy. In order to see more clearly the nature of the condition imposed on gravitational theory by this experiment, we must first broaden substantially the class of possible relativistic theories and then investigate the conditions imposed on this larger class by the Hughes–Drever experiment.

It is well known as a result of the investigations of Rosen[10], Gupta[11], Feynman[12], and Thirring[13] that the gravitational field can be treated within the framework of ordinary Lorentz invariant field theory as an ordinary zero-mass, chargeless tensor field. The interaction of matter with such a tensor field affects the matter, modifying it in such a way as to cause dilation of meter sticks and change of clock rates. As a result, such rods and clocks, made out of ordinary atoms interacting with such a field, do not provide a measure for the basic Minkowski tensor of this theory. This Minkowski tensor now becomes superfluous being replaced by the field tensor g_{ij} as the new metric tensor of the space.

Two things are clear from these papers. One is that the assumption of the Lorentz invariance of the theory is superfluous, for the Minkowski tensor is superfluous. Second, there is the implication that the gravitation may be, but need not be, considered as space geometry. It should be remarked parenthetically that in place of the Lorentz invariance of the theory associated with the original Minkowski tensor there is the usual local Lorentz invariance of a formalism based on the Riemannian metric tensor.

To recapitulate, a conclusion which can be obtained from these investigations is that the gravitational field can be, if desired, considered as a long range field interaction which affects rods and clocks, and hence the geometry measured by these rods and clocks. To interpret the gravitational field as an ordinary tensor interaction is a non-trivial re-interpretation for it opens the possibility of there being more than one long range interaction between neutral bodies, and it now becomes meaningful to consider other fields as contributing to the phenomenon we know as gravitation. As will become clear later the Hughes–Drever experiment sets a severe limit to possibilities of this type.

It may be desirable to say a philosophical word to the experts concerning this generalization. To the specialist working for years on general relativity, the Riemannian space of general relativity has gradually assumed a real and concrete form that belies its somewhat arbitrary character. Experts should be reminded of the remarks of Reichenbach, and of Poincaré before him, that the metric of a geometry is only in part a property of the space. It is equally a property of the particular type of measurement employed in the space. (Even the construction of the word "geometry" suggests that only half of this two part word "geo-metry" relates to the space, the remainder referring to its measurement.) To the extent that means of measure are arbitrary, the metrical properties of space are arbitrary.

Poincaré remarked that if surveying measurements showed space to be Riemannian, one could with equal right regard the space as flat and the meter stick distorted. This is a 3-dimensional nineteenth-century analogue of the Thirring calculation.

The general relativist accepts the general covariance of the theory as a necessary requirement because of the arbitrariness of the choice of coordinate system. However, usually he does not require a covariance associated with an arbitrariness in the choice of units of measure. Conformal transformations[14,15,16] induced by a redefinition of units, and for which units of length, time, and reciprocal mass are multiplied by a common, coordinate-dependent scale factor, constitute a restricted class of transformations of this type.

It is sometimes asserted that there is only one possible type of spatial measure in general relativity, and only one geometry, that given by ordinary meter sticks and clocks (or equivalently a measure based on the assumption of geodesic motion of neutral particles and null geodesics of light rays). However, it is possible to find counter examples and to give many alternative, if clumsy, definitions of the units of measure.

To give one example (a scale factor a function of the locally measured value of the scalar Maxwell invariant) could be applied locally to units of length, time, and reciprocal mass. As mentioned above, the resulting transformation of the metric tensor is conformal. Note that the scalar curvature is not invariant under such transformation.

While it could be argued with justification that these other arbitrarily defined systems of units are contrived, and of lesser importance than the usual one, which is the only one with physical significance, this is no longer true if there is more than one long range Boson field interacting with neutral matter.

Consider the following example: Assume that there exists, in addition to the electromagnetic and the gravitational long range fields, a scalar field φ, also long range (i.e., zero-mass).[17] It is assumed that the gravitational field tensor $\bar{g}_{ij}$ satisfies the Einstein field equation. It is known that the mass of a particle interacting with a scalar field is a function of the scalar, and that the equation of motion of such a particle, interacting with the scalar and the gravitational field but otherwise free, is obtained from the variational principle[15]

$$0 = \delta \int m(\varphi) \sqrt{-\bar{g}_{ij}u^i u^j} \, d\tau \; . \; u^i = (dx^i/d\tau) \tag{5}$$

If one writes,

$$m(\varphi) = mf(\varphi) \tag{6}$$

with m constant, the equation (5) can be written as

$$0 = \delta \int m \sqrt{-g_{ij}u^i u^j} \, d\tau \tag{7}$$

with

$$g_{ij} = \bar{g}_{ij} f^2. \tag{8}$$

Thus the particle moves on a geodesic trajectory associated with a new tensor g_{ij}. If matter of all kinds satisfies equation (6), then the new geodesic is the one that would be measured by real rods and clocks. Now comes the difficult decision: Should one define $\bar{g}_{ij}$, which satisfies Einstein's equation, as the metric tensor, or should one choose g_{ij}, measured by ordinary rods and clocks?

While the tensor $\bar{g}_{ij}$ may appear at first sight to be nonphysical, and to be an improper measure of the geometry, this is not true. It could be argued with considerable force that the "proper rods ·and clocks" are those adjusted to agree always with the "invariant length and time units" $(G\hbar/c^3)^{1/2}$ and $(G\hbar/c^5)^{1/2}$. One is forced to conclude that for this case there are at least two equally valid conformally related definitions of the metric tensor. In fact it might be argued that any two metric tensors, conformally related with the conformal factor an arbitrary function of φ, are equally valid definitions of the metric tensor, and that under such circumstances conformal covariance should appear in the theory.

The main point that is being made is that the usual interpretation of the gravitational field tensor as the metric tensor of a Riemannian geometry is a relatively unambiguous interpretation only if there are no other zero-mass Boson fields besides the gravitational field and electromagnetism. For purposes of discussion of the Hughes–Drever experiment, we might want to broaden the class of relativistic theories, and this might be most conveniently done by re-interpreting the gravitational field tensor g_{ij} as an ordinary tensor field and also permit other long range fields. In Appendix 4 we explore in more detail the implications of this particular approach to theories of gravitation. Its significance for cosmology is discussed in Appendix 5. The point of view adopted is different from that adopted by Rosen, Gupta, Feynman, and Thirring in that we do not introduce a flat space fundamental metric tensor. The geometrical substratum is initially limited to that of a differentiable manifold, without either an affine connection or a metric. Thus metric geometry is not introduced *a priori*.

Under some circumstances the mechanics of a Riemannian geometry is without interest for this class of gravitational theories. This can be easily seen by considering a simple example. Assume the existence of a second long range tensor field, i.e., a tensor additional to the first ordinary gravitational field tensor. Assume that such a tensor, generated by distant matter of the universe, and capable of penetrating the walls of the laboratory, interacts with the matter in the laboratory. Equations of motion of a free particle interacting only with the gravitational field and with this second tensor field can be obtained from the variational principle.

$$0 = \delta \int [m \sqrt{-g_{ij}u^iu^j} + \lambda \sqrt{-h_{ij}u^iu^j}] \, d\tau \tag{9}$$

where

$$d\tau^2 = -g_{ij} \, dx^i \, dx^j, \quad u^i = \frac{dx^i}{d\tau} \tag{10}$$

and λ, a constant, represents the coupling constant to the tensor field h_{ij}.

It should be noted that whereas the action integral for a particle coupling with a single tensor field may be taken, if desired, to be

$$0 = \delta \int m(-g_{ij}u^iu^j) \, d\tau \tag{11}$$

with $d\tau$ defined by equation (10), this form of the variational principle cannot be generalized to represent an interaction with two different tensor fields, being written in the form

$$0 = -\delta \int (mg_{ij} + \lambda h_{ij}) \, u^iu^j \, d\tau \tag{12}$$

unless variations are to be taken subject to the constraint represented by equation (10). Until this is done, the Euler equation is not consistent with the constraint condition. The necessity for a conditional variation can be relaxed if $d\tau$ is appropriately redefined. Equivalently, for any choice of $d\tau$, the variational integral might be taken as:

$$0 = \delta \int \sqrt{-(mg_{ij} + \lambda h_{ij}) \, u^iu^j} \, d\tau. \tag{13}$$

However, this integral is not linear in the two coupling constants (m, and λ). Also it represents a trivial decomposition of the metric tensor into two parts and does not represent the interaction of a particle with two different fields. The theories of Thirring and Gupta have elements of similarity. Roughly speaking, in these theories, the effective metric tensor g_{ij} is composed of two parts, one of which is η_{ij}, the Minkowski tensor, and the equations represent essentially a development in powers of $(g_{ij} - \eta_{ij})$ with appropriate coordinate conditions imposed. It is not surprising that η_{ij} is then unobservable.

On the other hand, the variational equation (9) is linear in the interactions with the two tensor fields (the resulting interactions are linearly superposable), and the constraint conditions, equation (10), are satisfied automatically. Because of the interaction with this tensor field, g_{ij} loses its character of being the metric tensor of the geometry obtained by measuring with real rods and clocks. One way to see this is to make the following substitution in equation (9)

$$
\begin{bmatrix}
u^i = \bar{u}^i \dfrac{d\bar{\tau}}{d\tau} \\[2mm]
d\tau = \dfrac{d\tau}{d\bar{\tau}} d\bar{\tau}
\end{bmatrix}
\text{ with }
\begin{bmatrix}
d\bar{\tau}^2 = -h_{ij}\, dx^i\, dx^j \\[2mm]
\bar{u}^i = (dx^i/d\bar{\tau}).
\end{bmatrix}
\tag{14}
$$

Then one has,

$$
0 = \delta \int [\lambda \sqrt{-h_{ij}\bar{u}^i\bar{u}^j} + m \sqrt{-g_{ij}\bar{u}^i\bar{u}^j}]\, d\bar{\tau}. \tag{15}
$$

Written in this completely equivalent form, h_{ij} now appears formally as a metric tensor of the geometry. Apparently neither of these geometries would be measured by rods and clocks made from such matter. In fact it can be easily shown that the equations of motion are not of the form of geodesic equations, and consequently the trajectory of the particle cannot be defined as the geodesic of a Riemannian geometry. Under these circumstances (i.e., with more than one tensor field) the introduction of the concepts of a Riemannian geometry into the physics of gravitation would be of little utility.

It might be wondered in what sense the above discussion is relevant to the experiments of Hughes and Drever. This has already been discussed by Peebles and Dicke[18], and more fully by Peebles[19]. The essential idea is that, whereas it is always possible to choose a coordinate system such that either g_{ij} or h_{ij} is locally Minkowskian with vanishing first derivatives, it is generally impossible to impose this condition simultaneously on both tensors. Hence there is generally no coordinate system, comoving with the laboratory, in which both g_{ij} and h_{ij} simultaneously exhibit spatial isotropy. Thus there is generally no coordinate system in which, locally, the Euler equations derived from equation (9) appear isotropic. It would then be expected that spatial anisotropy would occur in physical phenomena, contrary to what is observed by Hughes and Drever.

The Hughes–Drever experiment[6,7] is a null experiment of such precision that it would impose stringent limits upon any theory employing two zero-mass tensor fields. While the magnitude of these limits depends upon a detailed consideration of the theory in question, it is possible to illustrate the order of magnitude by considering a somewhat idealized version of the experiment and a simple model theory.

Let us imagine that the system upon which the experiment is being performed is an atom, the nucleus of which has only one nucleon, a proton, outside a closed shell and that in a $P_{3/2}$ state. We shall treat this nucleon as a classical particle interacting with the pion and electromagnetic fields of the nucleus, and also with two zero-mass tensor fields generated by the distant matter of the universe and propagated into the laboratory. Designating these fields by g_{ij} and h_{ij}, it will be assumed that they have the same signature and are normalized so that

$$\sqrt{-g} = \sqrt{-h}. \tag{16}$$

It will be assumed that the coupling to h_{ij} is very weak compared with that to g_{ij}. The various fields will be treated as known and given classical fields. The pion field will be treated for simplicity as a scalar field. The equations of motion of the proton are obtained from the variational principle

$$0 = \delta \int [m(\varphi) \sqrt{-g_{ij}u^i u^j} + \lambda(\varphi) \sqrt{-h_{ij}u^i u^j} + e A_i u^i]\, dx$$

$$u^i = \frac{dx^i}{dx} \text{ and with } \lambda \ll m. \tag{17}$$

The coupling of the magnetic moment of the proton to the electromagnetic field has been neglected, as has the spin interaction with the tensor fields.

The Euler equation derived from (17) is

$$0 = \frac{d}{d\chi} \left[\frac{mg_{ij}u^i}{\sqrt{-g_{jk}u^j u^k}} + \frac{\lambda h_{ij}u^j}{\sqrt{-h_{jk}u^j u^k}} \right] - \frac{1}{2} \left[\frac{mg_{ij,i}u^j u^k}{\sqrt{-g_{jk}u^j u^k}} + \frac{\lambda h_{jk,i}u^j u^k}{\sqrt{-h_{jk}u^j u^k}} \right]$$

$$+ \left[\frac{dm}{d\varphi} \sqrt{-g_{jk}u^j u^k} + \frac{d\lambda}{d\varphi} \sqrt{-h_{jk}u^j u^k} \right] \varphi_{,i} + e F_{ij}u^j. \tag{18}$$

This equation can be simplified by choosing the arbitrary χ to be proper time based on g_{ij} as a metric tensor. A further simplification is obtained by choosing the coordinate system to make g_{ij} locally Minkowskian. Further, in this coordinate system $g_{jk,j} = 0$ at the atom, and $h_{jk,i}$ will be neglected. This latter step is seen to be completely reasonable when it is remembered that gravitational forces are weak compared with nuclear forces. Simplifying in this way, it is seen that equation (18) becomes

$$0 = \frac{d}{d\tau} \left[m\eta_{ij}u^j + \frac{\lambda h_{ij}u^j}{\sqrt{-h_{jk}u^j u^k}} \right] + \left[\frac{dm}{d\varphi} + \frac{d\lambda}{d\varphi} \sqrt{-h_{jk}u^j u^k} \right] \varphi_{,i}$$

$$+ e F_{ij}u^j = 0. \tag{19}$$

Designating the first bracket by P_i, the kinetic momentum of the proton, it is seen that the momentum depends upon velocity in a complex way, and that because of the assumed 3-space anisotropy of the tensor h_{ij}, the connection is anisotropic. In similar fashion, if $d\lambda/d\varphi \neq 0$, the coupling to the pion field has a weak anisotropy. However, the electromagnetic coupling does not.

It is evident that equation (19) implies that the effective mass of the proton is direction dependent. Also the possible anisotropy of the pion coupling has a different direction and velocity dependence. It would be expected, therefore, that the orbital frequency would be orientation dependent.

In quantum mechanical terms, the proton, considered for the moment as spinless, moving in a P orbit would have its substates, normally degenerate in the absence of a magnetic field, split by the interaction with the tensor field.

By making a few simplifying assumptions it is easy to calculate explicitly the effect of the tensor h_{ij} on the energy states of the nucleus. First, it is assumed that h_{ij} has been reduced locally to diagonal form by a 3-space rotation and a Lorentz transformation. Then it is assumed that the externally applied magnetic field is along one of the principle axis of h_{ij}. Finally, the usual assumption is made, that nuclear states can be treated non-relativistically.

The first problem to formulate the quantum mechanical analogue of the dynamical problem represented by equation (17). To do this, a locally Minkowski coordinate system is again chosen, but this time χ is replaced by $x^4 = t$, coordinate time. In the usual way, the Hamiltonian function is now calculated to give

$$H = m + \lambda(-h_{44})^{1/2} + \frac{1}{2m}p^2 + \frac{1}{2m^2}\frac{\lambda}{(-h_{44})^{1/2}}h_{\alpha\beta}p^\alpha p^\beta + eA_4 \qquad (20)$$

α and β are summed over 1, 2, 3, only. The proton spin terms are missing as they were not present in equation (17). For simplicity the magnetic field is also neglected in equation (20). The effects of both magnetic fields and proton spin will be included later.

The spatial anisotropy effects are found only in the 4th term of the Hamiltonian. We are here explicitly assuming that there is no anisotropy in the distribution of either the electrostatic or pion fields. As $\lambda/m \ll 1$, the fourth term is treated as a perturbation only. To make the calculation particularly simple, it is assumed that the axis of quantization coincides with 1, 2, or 3, taken as (3) for definiteness. As discussed above we must calculate the effect on the 4 magnetic substates of the $P_{3/2}$ ground state of the interaction with h_{ij} and with the magnetic field. In perturbation theory the interaction with the tensor field is given by the expectation value

$$\left\langle \frac{\lambda}{2m^2(-h_{44})^{1/2}}h_{\alpha\beta}\,p^\alpha p^\beta \right\rangle. \qquad (21)$$

As the coordinate dependence of m and λ is purely radial, these terms contribute nothing to the m_j dependence of this expectation value. The m_j dependence of the diagonal matrix elements of the square of the component of a vector is well known. Hence, the essential features of equation (21) can be seen by inspection. It is helpful in this connection to make the substitution

$$h_{\alpha\beta}p_\alpha p_\beta = \tfrac{1}{2}(h_{11}+h_{22})[p_1^2 + p_2^2 + p_3^2] + \tfrac{1}{2}(h_{11}-h_{22})[p_1^2 - p_2^2]$$
$$+ [h_{33} - \tfrac{1}{2}(h_{11}+h_{22})]\,p_3^3. \qquad (22)$$

The expectation value of the first term on the right is clearly independent of m_j. That of the second vanishes as $\langle p_1^2 \rangle = \langle p_2^2 \rangle$. Hence, dropping terms independent of m_j, we have

$$\left\langle \frac{\lambda}{2m^2(-h_{44})^{1/2}}h_{\alpha\beta}p^\alpha p^\beta \right\rangle = \frac{h_{33} - \tfrac{1}{2}(h_{11}+h_{22})}{(-h_{44})^{1/2}}\left\langle \frac{\lambda}{2m^2}p_3^2 \right\rangle$$
$$= \left(\frac{1}{2} - \frac{2}{15}m_j^2\right).\frac{h_{33} - \tfrac{1}{2}(h_{11}+h_{22})}{(-h_{44})^{1/2}}\left\langle \frac{\lambda}{2m^2}p^2 \right\rangle. \qquad (23)$$

This is most conveniently written by taking (λ/m) outside the integral as the appropriate mean value.

The perturbation of the m_j energy state by the magnetic field and the tensor field can be written as:

$$\Delta E_{mj} = m_j B + \left(\frac{1}{2} - \frac{2}{15}m_j{}^2\right)\frac{h_{33} - \frac{1}{2}(h_{11} + h_{22})}{(-h_{44})^{1/2}}\left\langle\frac{\lambda}{m}\right\rangle\left\langle\frac{1}{2m}p^2\right\rangle. \qquad (24)$$

It should be noted that the effect of interaction with the tensor field is one of raising the two $m_j = \pm \frac{1}{2}$ states relative to the $3/2$ states by

$$\frac{4}{15}\frac{h_{33} - \frac{1}{2}(h_{11} + h_{22})}{(-h_{44})^{1/2}}\left\langle\frac{\lambda}{m}\right\rangle\left\langle\frac{1}{2m}p^2\right\rangle. \qquad (25)$$

If the radial dependence of λ is no stronger than that of m, the first mean value can be neglected. The second mean represents the average kinetic energy of the proton. If

$$|h_{33} - \tfrac{1}{2}(h_{11} + h_{22})| \geq 1 \qquad (26)$$

we may say that the h field is "strongly anisotropic." In this case we can write

$$\frac{\lambda}{m(-h_{44})^{1/2}} \geq \frac{15}{4}\frac{\Delta\epsilon}{\left\langle\frac{1}{2m}p^2\right\rangle} \qquad (27)$$

where $\Delta\epsilon$ is the largest energy shift that would not have been observed by Drever[7]. This was 0.04 cycles/sec or 2.5×10^{-28} ergs. Taking the mean value of the kinetic energy as 10Mev or 2×10^{-5} ergs, we obtain

$$\frac{\lambda}{m(-h_{44})^{1/2}} \leq \frac{15}{4}\,1.3 \times 10^{-23} = 4.5 \times 10^{-23}. \qquad (28)$$

But the left side of this equation represents the ratio of the strengths of coupling to the h and g fields. Clearly with the assumptions that the h field is strongly anisotropic its coupling must be extremely weak.

At this point there is an important question to be answered. If protons were to couple with the tensor field h_{ij}, so also might pions and photons. (See reference 9 for a discussion of this point.) As a result, the pion and photon fields might also be distorted by this tensor field. Is it possible for the couplings to the various fields to be such that the effects of the various distortions cancel out, there being no observable effect?

It will be argued that this would not occur, that distortions of the pion and electromagnetic fields that cancel the observable anisotropy effects for one state of the nucleus would be ineffective for another state. While the argument is not as firm as one would like, it is elementary. To reduce it to its simplest terms we neglect the electromagnetic field and assume that $h_{4\alpha} = 0$, $\alpha = 1, 2, 3$. Consider first a state where the proton moves with non-relativistic velocities. For this state the second term in the definition of kinetic momentum

$$p_i = m\eta_{ij}u^j + \lambda\frac{h_{ij}u^j}{\sqrt{-h_{jk}u^ju^k}} \qquad (29)$$

is very small compared with the first (since $\lambda \ll m$). Hence a very small anisotropy in the pion field is sufficient to compensate for the presence of this second term. Consider the two terms in equation (29) at relativistic velocities.

The denominator of the second term of equation (29) is the square root of a quadratic form in u^i. Consider the value of this denominator as a function of the 3-vector u^α, $\alpha = 1, 2, 3$. The possibility that it goes uniformly to a finite value as $u^\alpha \to \infty$ can be excluded, as this would require that h_{ij} be η_{ij} to within a constant factor. Also there may or may not be 2 dimensional surfaces on which the denominator vanishes in the finite space. If such surfaces exist, they bound non-physical regions of u^α space in which the denominator is imaginary. We can now consider two cases depending upon whether or not such surfaces exist. If they exist there are vales of u^α for which the second term in equation (29) is large compared with the first. On the other hand, if they do not exist, the second term vanishes uniformly in comparison with the first as $u^\alpha \to \infty$.

We may safely assume that in the first case, when the second term in equation (29) is large, the weak anisotropy of the two Boson fields is insufficient to compensate for the resulting large anisotropy in the momentum velocity relation. In the second case, the momentum anisotropy disappears as $u^i \to \infty$, whereas that of the fields does not. Apparently an anisotropy (in principle observable) should occur if an atom interacts with two zero-mass tensor fields.

It is necessary to remark that h_{ij}, generated by a spherical universe, would be expected to be diagonal with the space-like components all equal in a coordinate system exhibiting this symmetry. In this case the spatial anisotropy is missing except for the small contributions from nearby matter. On the other hand, this spatial isotropy is destroyed by a Lorentz transformation and there should be observable effects on the earth, assumed to be moving relative to this coordinate system.

To summarize this discussion we can say that the Hughes–Drever experiment appears to exclude a coupling to two zero-mass tensor fields (cosmological in origin). If two fields are present with the one strongly anisotropic, in a coordinate system chosen to make the other isotropic, the strength of coupling to one must be only of the order of 10^{-22} that of the other. If some cancellation of this anisotropy should occur through an appropriate anisotropy of the other fields, this cancellation would be expected to be incomplete, depending upon the state of the nucleus. If both tensor fields should be isotropic simultaneously, this condition would be destroyed by Lorentz transformation. Hence on the moving earth with ever changing velocity, anisotropy would be expected at some season. We conclude that the presence of a second tensor field is very unlikely in view of the experiments of Hughes and Drever.

The Ether Drift Experiments

The remaining null experiments requiring discussion may be crudely labeled as ether drift experiments, for the prototype of these experiments was that of Michelson and Morely, which was motivated by the nineteenth century ether concept.

One might rashly judge such experiments to be antirelativity in conception, but such is far from the case. There is a definite observable difference between a laboratory moving with respect to the universe and one which is not. Namely, in the first case galaxies are *observed* to stream toward us in one direction and away from us in the opposite direction. Any non-scalar field generated by this distant matter, in addition to the basic gravitational tensor, could produce motional effects. Consider a non-gauge-invariant vector field which couples with matter so weakly as to be compatible with the Eötvös experiment but which, for some reason, is strong as a component of the cosmological background. In the comoving coordinate systems for which the universe appears everywhere isotropic, this vector field must have only one non-zero component D_4 which is a function of x^4 only and hence for which $F_{ij} = 0$. Such a field could not introduce a guage invariant interaction, but there, are many coupling schemes which are not gauge invariant, e.g., $(A_i U^i D_j U^j)^{1/2}$, representing a joint interaction of a charged particle with an electromagnetic field and this cosmic field. It is easily seen that the motion of the laboratory with respect to such a vector field could lead to observable effects: positive results for an experiment such as that by Michelson and Moreley.

Of the various null experiments of this type, the most interesting and one of the most precise was carried out recently by a Princeton student, K. Turner[24], under the supervision mainly of Prof. H. Hill. It is particularly interesting, as it incorporates nuclear forces, strong electromagnetic forces in the nucleus, the electron structure of the atom, and the propagation of photons as ingredients which could conceivably disturb the null result.

While this is the most interesting of the null experiments of this type, it has not yet been published and consequently has had no publicity. In view of its importance, I am happy to take the opportunity to say something about the experiment. (Has since been published, *Phys. Rev.*, **134**, 252 (1964).)

It started out about September 1959 as an attempt to measure the gravitational red shift using the Mössbauer effect which had just been discovered, but it soon became apparent that there were two other groups working on this problem, and to avoid a horse race it was dropped about November in favor of the one to be described.

In this experiment, a cobalt 57 source was placed near the rim of a standard centrifuge wheel, roughly 25 cm in diameter, with an iron 57 absorber near the axis, the line joining the two passing through the axis but making an angle with it of about 60°. At the point of intersection on the axis, above the wheel, a thin sodium iodide scintilator was mounted on the wheel. The light from the scintilator was carried through a lucite light pipe, fixed to the wheel, to a non-rotating photomultiplier mounted above the wheel. The pulses from the photomultiplier were separated by a single channel analyzer into two categories representing the 14·4 kev. γ ray (narrow) and the broad 122 kev radiation. These two types of γ ray counts were chaneled into four groups of two scalers each to count both γ rays simultaneously in each of four quadrants of the wheel's position.

As the wheel rotated, four tiny mirrors on its periphery were used to operate electronic switches to channel the counts occurring in each 90° of rotation into separate channels. Thus, the two scalers into which counts were dumped in the first 90° of rotation of the wheel totaled up for this same quadrant all the counts accumulated in a long period of counting.

We shall now describe the experiment. For simplicity in thinking about the problem we shall concentrate on only one aspect of it, and mention other aspects later. Consider the nucleus to be thought of as a clock. If its proper clock rate is a function of its velocity relative to the distant matter of the universe, it would be expected to vary in lowest order quadratically with the velocity. This is made a meaningful statement by making the comparison with a fixed clock of the same type using light pulses for the intercomparison.

This is effectively what the apparatus does. With the assumption that the electronic structure behaves in a proper Lorentz-invariant way and that light propagates on null geodesics, the γ ray from the source at the rim of the wheel may be compared directly with the absorber near the axis, after making allowance for the second order Doppler shift.

The second order Doppler shift is actually important for the experiment. Because of this effect the radiation from the source is red shifted substantially, and the probability of transmission through the filter varies linearly with any further shift (very small). If it were not for the initial shift induced either by the Doppler effect, a temperature difference, or some other cause, the effect would be quadratic in the frequency shift, hence unobservable.

Because of the velocity **u** of the laboratory relative to distant matter, the Mössbauer clock at the rim of the wheel has a time varying velocity **u** + **v**, and the clock rate should vary with the angular position of the wheel as

$$\frac{\delta\omega}{\omega} = 2\gamma u v \cos\theta. \tag{21}$$

Here v refers to the peripheral speed of the wheel, and the angle θ is that between the source velocity vector and the component of **u** lying in the plane of the wheel. The magnitude of this component is designated by **u**. The γ is some small dimensionless number, a measure of the magnitude of the effect, if any.

As the wheel rotates, counts are accumulated for each of four quadrants, and the ratio of the 14·4 kev counts to the 122 kev counts is taken to be a measure of the shift $\delta\omega/\omega$ (averaged over that quadrant). The actual numerical relation between change in count ratio and $\delta\omega/\omega$ is easily obtained from the known line width and shape, after including the shift due to the second order Doppler effect.

The best data were obtained from 134 runs of about 10-minute duration taken at various times of the day between October 24, 1961, and November 11, 1961. This represented a total of 4×10^6 14·4 kev counts and 5×10^7 122 kev counts.

As the earth rotates, any effect of a component of **u** lying in the equatorial plane of the earth would rotate spatially relative to the laboratory producing an anomaly, the axis of which would rotate in the laboratory. By making a least squares fit to the expected time dependence of the anomaly, it was possible to give γ a value

$$\gamma < 4·2 \times 10^{-5} \tag{22}$$

with the assumption that the component of **u** in the equatorial plane is 200 km/sec with an unknown direction. The assumption of 200 km/sec is of course arbitrary, but it is reasonable. The random motions of galaxies are of this order, as is the motion of the sun inside our own galaxy. Another way of describing the result is to quote γu, which gives 840 cm/sec as an upper limit on this, the classical "ether drift velocity."

Inasmuch as both photon propagation and the mechanical structure of the wheel were involved in this experiment, it also sets limits on possible anomalies in these parts of the apparatus. The analysis would be very similar to that of the effect on the proper clock rate.

II. Three Famous Tests of General Relativity

The Gravitational Red Shift

As discussed above, this is not a test of anything but energy conservation and mass-energy equivalence. While it is possible with a second tensor interaction to violate the mass-energy equivalence,[18,19] the Hughes[6]–Drever[7] experiment seems to exclude this.

While this experiment may not be the most important of relativity experiments, it is interesting, and I should like to discuss briefly the experiment of one of my students, J. Brault, on the red shift of solar lines.[25]

This subject has had a long and checkered career going back to the earliest days of general relativity. After some early misguided enthusiasm, it soon became clear that the solar spectral lines did not give the expected red shift (some were actually blue shifted). One particularly annoying feature of the red shift was that it was strongly dependent on how close to the limb of the sun one observed. At the center of the sun the shift tended not to appear, although different lines gave different shifts. At the limb the shifts tended to agree better with expectations.

At first these shifts were explained as pressure effects, with the shifts being larger at the center of the sun because the lines were formed deeper in the atmosphere. It became clear finally that the center-limb shifts were primarily due to the Doppler effects associated with the convective transport of heat out of the sun. Deep in the sun this energy is transported by radiation, but it is convectively transported in the outer part until near the surface, insofar as the sun can be said to have a surface, it is again transported by radiation. The Doppler effect of the hot rising columns and cool falling gas leads to the irregularly shifted lines.

While the astronomer's knowledge of the surface of the sun improved enormously in the past forty years, the determination of the red shift, worked on almost constantly by different spectroscopists during this period of time, improved very little.

In my opinion this lack of progress was largely due to their use of the wrong instrument. The photographic plate is a wonderful device for conveniently recording a lot of information on a small plate but is dreadful at providing a quantitative measure of light intensity. In the language of the experimentalist, it has poor "signal to noise." Because of this poor intensity discrimination due to grain, lack of plate uniformity, lack of development uniformity, and other causes, these classical techniques were incapable of giving a precise measure of the center of a broad line unless it showed a narrow "core."

We made the assumption that a very broad spectral line would be developed in the solar atmosphere above the main convective troubles, and hence be free of systematic Doppler shifts. (It should be remarked that the "wings" of the line would still be developed deep in the sun and that they would be expected to experience strong Doppler shifts which would not average to zero). Dr. Brault was able to show that with the proper spectrometer, averaging over reasonably large areas, the line position of a strong line agreed with the expected value and did not show any noticeable center-limb shift.

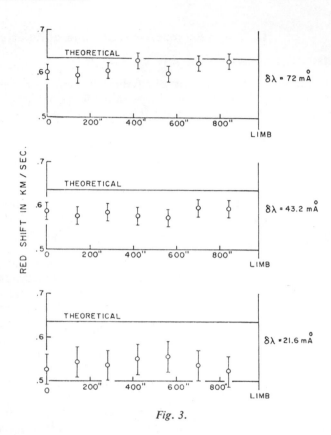

Fig. 3.

It occurred to us that the sodium D lines were ideally suited for the red shift measurement. The lines were strong; sodium had a good abundance; it was easily ionized at high temperatures removing this part of the sodium from the game; thus, the rapidly moving very high temperature parts of the upper atmosphere should not contribute.

The ideal line for this purpose was found to be the D_1 line of sodium.

In order to measure with precision the center of the line, a special instrument was required. This was designed and built by Dr. Brault and it worked beautifully. It consisted of a two-pass grating instrument employing three slits, the third one of which was broad, designed to remove ghosts (false lines). The middle slit could be displaced and oscillated by an electromechanical device. The light was detected by a photomultiplier, and the line center was defined by the requirement that the slit oscillation frequency disappear from the output voltage of the photomultiplier whenever the mean position of the slit agreed with line center. It is evident that, if the line is asymmetric, a correction is needed for the effect of the asymmetry. This can be obtained by making observations at various amplitudes of oscillation if the asymmetry is known. In similar fashion a correction for the asymmetries of the spectrometer is required.

The spectrometer, as it was designed by Dr. Brault, located ˙electronically the line "center" and automatically locked the mean position of the oscillating slit to the line center. This line "center" was automatically recorded electronically as the image of the sun swept across the entrance slit. The raw data, uncorrected for asymmetries, is shown in Fig. 3 for 3 amplitudes of oscillation $\delta\lambda$. It should be noted that even without correction the agreement is better than 20 per cent. It should also be noted that the center-limb shift has disappeared. After correction for asymmetries the red shift was found to agree with the expected result with an accuracy of 5 per cent (noise limited). It should finally be remarked that the secondary laboratory standard used was a sodium lamp which was compared with a sodium absorption cell as a primary standard.

This appears to be one of the two best determinations of the red shift. The other is the determination by Pound and Rebka[26] using the Mössbauer effect. Its accuracy was 10 per cent.

The Gravitational Deflection of Light

The gravitational deflection of light is an observation which is more important for gravitation. This effect depends upon other components of the gravitational tensor besides g_{44}, in the usual coordinate system of the Schwarzschild problem. Unfortunately, the accuracy of this observation is poor. The analyses scatter from a deflection at the limb of the sun of $1\cdot43$ seconds of arc to $2\cdot7''$ ($1\cdot75''$ computed). The scatter would not be too bad if one could believe that the technique was free of systematic errors. It appears that one must consider this observation uncertain to at least 10 per cent, and perhaps as much as 20 per cent.

The Perihelion Rotation of Mercury

The third and final one of these tests is even more important as it involves the g_{44} component to second order in GM/r and the other components to first order. Unfortunately, it also is uncertain. This is because of an uncertainty in the gravitational quadrupole moment of the sun.

On the surface this check appears to be very satisfactory. The most recent results are the following[(27)]:

	Mercury	Venus	Earth
Observed	$43''\cdot11 \pm \cdot45$	$8''\cdot4 \pm 4\cdot8$	$5''\cdot0 \pm 1''\cdot2$
Calc.	$43''\cdot03$	$8''\cdot3$	$3''\cdot8$

These are perihelion rotations in seconds of arc per century. In saying that these are observed effects it is necessary to remark that what is observed is far larger. The observed rotation is 120 times as great for Mercury, 600 times as great for Venus, and 1200 times as great for the Earth. From these large effects it is necessary to subtract the geometrical effect of the general precession of the equinoxes and the effects of planetary perturbations. It is only a small residual that is to be compared with the calculated relativistic effect.

Unfortunately, only the planet Mercury provides a sensitive test of this relativistic effect. The interaction with Venus was, and may still be, the largest source of uncertainty in the non-relativistic perturbation of Mercury's orbit. Venus does not have a satellite, and its mass can be determined only from its perturbations of other planets, such as Mercury. Obviously, this is a somewhat circular argument if we must first use the perturbations to determine adopted planetary masses and then use these masses to calculate orbits.

The uncertainty concerning the mass of Venus seems recently to have been reduced substantially by the Venus fly-by of the American planetoid. The orbit was sufficiently accurately determined to permit a better determination of the mass of Venus. This substantially reduces the possibility of a serious discrepancy in this adopted mass. Hence, it appears that we must accept this "observed" result if the only substantial perturbations are due to other planets.

Let us consider other possible sources of matter for a perturbation of Mercury's orbit. These have been considered as long ago as 1928 by J. Chazy[28]. The solar corona could not have enough matter to be important without scattering more light. The matter responsible for the zodiacal light, assumed to be meteorite-like bodies, is not sufficient. For the same scattering of light, dust is even less effective in perturbing the orbit. The way to get the most matter for the least scattered light is to put it into one body.

The size of body required, near the sun, is so great as to be visible. It appears that matter exterior to the sun sufficient to be important is not easily found. Actually, these old discussions should be reexamined, particularly the possibility of a few small asteroid bodies near the sun. The reason for this is the following: If gravitation is due to a combination of a tensor and scalar interaction, the expected perihelion rotation is somewhat less. Even a 5 per cent decrease would be significant and interesting. The classical considerations were concerned with explaining the whole discrpancy. We are concerned with the possibility of a discrepancy of the order of 5–20 per cent.

There is one possible source of discrepancy which seems to be very serious. A solar flattening amounting to a decrease of the polar radius by only 0·1″ of arc relative to the equatorial radius would result in a non-relativistic contribution to the rotation of 8·3″ arc per century, 20 per cent of the relativistic effect. It must be said in making this statement that it is assumed that the visual surface of the sun represents an equal pressure surface which is also assumed to be an equipotential surface for the gravitational field. If these assumptions are valid, the gravitational field is known everywhere outside this photosphere, once its shape is known.

It must be recognized that there are uncertainties about these assumptions. First, a small variation in brightness of the photosphere in the vicinity of the pole relative to the equator would modify the connection between isophote lines and equipressure surfaces. Second, it is only in the absence of shear stresses and velocity field gradients at the surface that the equipotential surface is identical with the equipressure surface.

Magnetic fields are capable of exerting shear stresses, and velocity fields are known to exist. Both of these effects appear to be minor but a close study will be necessary before one can be sure.

It appears that the interior of the sun is not so well known that a solar flattening as large as $0 \cdot 1''$ arc, $\Delta\gamma/\gamma \sim 10^{-4}$, can be excluded. This could be produced by a rapidly rotating core in the sun, or by toroidal magnetic fields, which are capable of large stress but are not seen at the surface.

It is now necessary to say a word about the possibility of observing a flattening as small as 10^{-4}. This appears to be definitely measurable, but not with the classical techniques of the astronomers. The bad daytime seeing smears out the limb of the sun by several seconds of arc and we are interested in only $0 \cdot 1''$ arc. An experiment has been started at Princeton to attempt to set limits on the solar oblateness but results are not yet available.

It is reasonable to ask if a quadrupole moment of the sun would not have other effects on the planets besides rotation of their perihelions. Here we have been very unfortunate. A flattening of only 10^{-4} ($0 \cdot 1''$ arc) has no other effects presently observable. The axis of the sun is tipped only $3 \cdot 3°$ with respect to the plane of Mercury's orbit. The resulting torque is small but is sufficient to produce a slow wobble of the orbit. This leads to the expectation that the inclination of Mercury's orbit would decrease anomalously by $0 \cdot 16''$ of arc per century (for a flattening of 10^{-4}). This apparently cannot be excluded by the observations, for an anomalous decrease of about this size is known, but with comparable probable error.

Unfortunately, we are also unlucky with respect to Venus' orbit. Here again the effect is small, even smaller because the planet is farther out. The angle between the normal to the orbital plane of Venus and the rotational axis of the sun is about $4°$. Here the effect is almost completely one of producing a small anomalous motion in the node of Venus.

By the time we reach the earth's orbit the inclination of the sun's axis is a full $7°15'$, but we are now so far out that the effect of this coupling is very small. We are forced to conclude that there is not yet believable observational evidence that can be used to exclude a discrepancy as large as 10–20 per cent in the relativistic part of the perihelion rotation of Mercury. It seems very unsafe to argue on the basis of theories of the sun's interior that an oblateness as large as 10^{-4} is impossible.

It is unfortunate that both the light deflection and perihelion rotation observations are so uncertain, for these are the only data which could be used to exclude gravitational theories incorporating both scalar and tensor fields[21]. In the Brans–Dicke theory, a value of the constant $\omega \geq 2$ now seems possible with the new large uncertainty in the perihelion rotation.

Cosmic Experiments

There are literally thousands of observations of geophysical and astrophysical nature which might be used to exclude a theory such as that discussed in Ref. 21. However, it is virtually impossible to use this type of data to "prove" such a theory. Of course, one never proves a theory with an experiment, for a better experiment

8

can always prove it wrong. However, astrophysical and geophysical data are particularly suspect, for the earth, the solar system, a star, and the galaxy are all too complicated to be used to support strongly a physical theory. There are too many loopholes in the form of alternative explanations.

On the other hand, a physicist ignores such data at his peril, for they can supply him with useful ideas including, perhaps, a fairly convincing reason for dropping the theory.

We make no attempt here to rediscuss those questions which are taken up in Appendices (9), (10), (11), and (12).

Summary and conclusion. The following point of view was adopted: For purposes of discussing relativity experiments, one should consider a somewhat wider theoretical framework than one would normally like, and experiments should be used to limit this class of possible theories.

In this connection it was found helpful to treat gravitation as a particle field, and to subordinate the geometrical interpretation. The possibility that the gravitational effect could be due to two or more long range fields was considered. The following points occurred:

(1) The primary gravitational effect is, perhaps, due entirely to a zero mass tensor interaction if Mach's principle is valid; for the inertial forces are acceleration dependent and a Lagrangian quadratic in the velocity is needed for acceleration terms to appear in the Euler equations.

(2) A tensor plus vector theory of gravitation seems unlikely because of the precise null result of the Eötvös experiment.

(3) A two-tensor theory of gravitation can be excluded by the Hughes–Drever experiment.

(4) A tensor plus scalar field affecting the fine structure constant or other strong coupling constants can be excluded by the Eötvös experiment.

(5) A tensor plus scalar field coupled to the weak coupling constant cannot be excluded.

(6) A tensor plus scalar coupled to only some types of particles can be excluded by the Eötvös experiment.

(7) A tensor plus scalar coupled in the same way to all kinds of particles cannot be excluded.

(8) A tensor plus scalar interacting with each other but not with other particles cannot be excluded.

(9) The theories of the tensor plus scalar types (Jordan) cannot be all excluded easily. They violate only the light deflection and perihelion rotation effects, and these observations are too poor to represent strong results.

In conclusion, there is a real challenge for the experimentalist to exclude or else to find the scalar component of the gravitational field.

References

1. Wapstra, A. H. and Nijgh, G. J. 1955, *Physica*, **21**, 796.
2. Dicke, R. H. 1959, *Science*, **129**, 621.
3. Landau, L. in *Niels Bohr and The Development of Physics*, edited by W. Pauli (McGraw-Hill Book Co., New York, 1955).

4. Schiff, L. I. 1959, *Proc. Nat. Acad. Science*, **45**, 69.
5. Eötvös, R. V., Pekar, D. and Fekete, E. 1922, *Ann. Phys.*, **68**, 11.
6. Hughes, V. W., Robinson, H. G. and Beltran-Lopez, V. 1960, *Phys. Rev. Letters*, **4**, 342.
7. Drever, R. W. P. 1961, *Phil. Mag.*, **6**, 683.
8. Cocconi G. and Salpeter, E. E. 1958, *Nuovo Cimento*, **10**, 646; 1960, *Phys. Rev. Letters*, **4**, 176.
9. Dicke, R. H. 1961, *Phys. Rev. Letters*, **7**, 359 (see appendix 1).
10. Rosen, N. 1940, *Phys. Rev.* **57**, 147.
11. Gupta, S. 1957, *Rev. Mod. Phys.* **29**, 334.
12. Feynman, R. 1957, Chapel Hill Conference.
13. Thirring, W. E. 1961, *Annals of Phys.*, **16**, 96–117.
14. Schouten J. A. and Haantjes, J. 1940, *Koninkl. Ned. Akad. Wetenschap, Proc.*, **43**, 1288.
15. Dicke, R. H. 1962, *Phys. Rev.* **125**, 2163 (see appendix 2).
16. Fulton, T., Rohrlich, F. and Witten, L. 1962, *Rev. Mod. Phys.*, **34**, 442.
17. Dicke, R. H. 1962, *Phys. Rev.*, **126**, 1785 (see appendix 5).
18. Peebles, J. and Dicke, R. H. 1962, *Phys. Rev.* **127**, 629 (see appendix 6).
19. Peebles, J. 1962, *Annals of Phys.*, **20**, 240.
20. King, J. G. 1960, *Phys. Rev. Letters*, **5**, 562.
21. Brans, C. and Dicke, R. H. 1961, *Phys. Rev.*, **124**, 925. (see appendix 7).
22. Lee, T. D. and Yang, C. N. 1955, *Phys. Rev.*, **98**, 1501.
23. Dicke, R. H. 1962, *Phys. Rev.* **126**, 1580 (see appendix 8).
24. Turner, K. 1962, Thesis, Princeton University.
25. Brault, J. 1962, Thesis, Princeton University.
26. Pound, R. V. and Rebka, G. A. 1960, *Phys. Rev. Letters*, **4**, 337.
27. Duncombe, R. L. 1956, *Astron. J.*, **61**, 174.
28. Chazy, J. 1928, *La théorie del a relativité et la méchanique céleste*, Paris.

Appendices

(1) Dicke, R. H. 1961, "Experimental Tests of Mach's Principle," *Phys. Rev. Letters* **7**, 359.
(2) Dicke, R. H. 1962, "Mach's Principle and Invariance under Transformation of Units," *Phys. Rev.*, **125**, 2163.
(3) Dicke, R. H. 1962, "Long-Range Scalar Interaction," *Phys. Rev.*, **126**, 1875.
(4) Field Theories of Gravitation.
(5) Dicke, R. H., 1963, "Cosmology, Mach's Principle and Relativity," *I.C.S.U. Review*, **5**, 40.
(6) Peebles, P. J. and Dicke, R. H., 1962, "Significance of Spatial Isotropy," *Phys. Rev.*, **127**, 629.
(7) Brans, C. and Dicke, R. H., 1961, "Mach's Principle and a Relativistic Theory of Gravitation," *Phys. Rev.*, **124**, 925.
(8) Dicke, R. H., 1962, "Lee-Yang Vector Field and Isotropy of the Universe," *Phys. Rev.*, **126**, 1580.
(9) Dicke, R. H., 1962, "The Earth and Cosmology," *Science*, **138**, 653.
(10) Dicke, R. H., 1962, "Implications for Cosmology of Stellar and Galactic Evolution Rates," *Revs. Modern Phys.*, **34**, 110.
(11) Dicke, R. H., 1962, "Dating the Galaxy by Uranium Decay," *Nature*, **194**, 329.
(12) Dicke, R. H., 1959, "Dirac's Cosmology and the Dating of Meteorites," *Nature*, **183**, 170.

Appendix I

Experimental Tests of Mach's Principle*

R. H. Dicke

Reprinted from *Phys. Rev. Letters* **7**, 359, (1961)

In this note it will be shown that, contrary to the suggestion of Cocconi and Salpeter,[1] the extremely precise null result of the experiments of Hughes, Robinson,

* This research was supported in part by the Office of Naval Research, the U.S. Atomic Energy Commission, and the Higgins Scientific Trust Fund.

and Beltrow–Lopez[2] and Drever[3] is to be expected, resulting from an application of Mach's principle.

According to Mach's principle, as formulated by Bishop Berkeley,[4] Mach,[5] and Sciama,[6] the inertial forces experienced in an accelerated laboratory are gravitational, having their origin in the distant matter of the universe, accelerated relative to the laboratory. Because of the tensor character of the gravitational-inertial field, it should exhibit tensor polarization properties. In particular, as suggested by Cocconi and Salpeter, because of the flattened rotating mass distribution of our galaxy, the inertial reaction having its origin in this mass distribution should exhibit some spatial anisotropy. This should appear in the formalism as a tensor inertial mass. Cocconi and Salpeter suggested that if Mach's principle were valid, the effects of this tensor inertial mass would appear as a spatial anisotropy in certain experiments. Several experiments, designed to test Mach's principle in this way, have been performed or analyzed.[1–3,7] By far the most accurate has been that of Drever.[3]

It will be shown that the experiments do not represent a test of Mach's principle in the manner suggested by Cocconi and Salpeter. On the contrary, and in agreement with the requirements of Mach's principle, the experiments show that, with great precision, the anisotropy of the inertial mass is universal, the same for all particles.

Expressed relativistically, the suggestion of Cocconi and Salpeter[1] is that the four-momentum of a particle can be written as

$$P_i = m_{ij}u^j, \tag{1}$$

where u^i is the four-velocity of the particle. In the absence of a gravitational field, the particle is assumed to obey the equations of motion,

$$dP_i/ds = F_i, \tag{2}$$

where F_i is the four-force acting on the particle and as usual F_i satisfies the condition

$$F_i u^i = 0. \tag{3}$$

As Mach's principle associates the inertial reaction with the matter distribution in the universe, an anisotropy in the inertial mass should be universal, the same for all particles at the same space-time location, for all particles would see the same mass distribution. With the assumption that the inertial reaction is universal, the tensor m_{ij} can be expressed as

$$m_{ij} = mf_{ij}, \tag{4}$$

where f_{ij} is a universal tensor field (dimensionless).

A serious objection to equations (1)–(4) can be raised. Equations (2) and (3) are generally not consistent with the constraint condition,

$$g_{ij}u^i u^i = u^i u_i = 1. \tag{5}$$

Consistent equations can be obtained from a variational principle. We note that to generate a momentum such as equation (1), linear in a four-velocity, a first condition to be satisfied is that the Lagrangian of the particle should be a function of the invariant

$$(d\bar{s}/ds)^2 = f_{ij}u^iu^j. \tag{6}$$

Equations of motion of a free particle (gravitational forces only) are obtained from the variational principle,

$$0 = \delta \int L ds, \tag{7}$$

where variations of the coordinates are to be taken subject to the constraint, equation (5). With the assumption that f_{ij} and g_{ij} are not equivalent, the resulting expression for the four-momentum is linear in some four-velocity only for the unique choice,

$$L = m(f_{ij}u^iu^j)^{1/2}. \tag{8}$$

With this choice, the constraint condition, equation (5), is satisfied by the equations of motion automatically, without introducing the condition of constraint in the variational calculation. As a result, the equations of motion do not contain g_{ij} explicitly.

Substituting equation (8) in equation (7), the equations of motion of a free particle are

$$\frac{d}{ds} \frac{m_{ij}u^j}{(f_{ki}u^ku^j)^{1/2}} - \tfrac{1}{2} \frac{m_{jk,i}u^ju^k}{(f_{kj}u^ku^j)^{1/2}} = 0. \tag{9}$$

These are most conveniently expressed, introducing f_{ij} as a new metric tensor, by defining

$$d\bar{s}^2 = f_{ij}dx^idx^j, \tag{10}$$

$$\bar{u}^i = dx^i/d\bar{s}. \tag{11}$$

With these substitutions, equation (9) becomes

$$\frac{d}{d\bar{s}} (m_{ij}\bar{u}^j) - \tfrac{1}{2}m_{jk,i}\bar{u}^j\bar{u}^k = 0. \tag{12}$$

The resulting particle trajectories are geodesics of the new geometry, with f_{ij} as metric tensor. The limiting trajectories of particles with infinite energy are null geodesics of the new geometry.

Inasmuch as g_{ij} does not appear explicitly in the classical equations of motion of a particle, the appropriate quantum mechanical wave equations, giving equations of motion of expectation values equivalent to the classical equations, are constructed by employing f_{ij} as the metric tensor. For example, the appropriate Lagrangian density for the Klein–Gordon wave function is

$$\tfrac{1}{2}\hbar^2 f^{ij}\varphi_{,i}\varphi_{,j} - \tfrac{1}{2}m^2\varphi^2. \tag{13}$$

It may be noted with the assumption made above, that the inertial reaction is universal, the same for all particles including photons and pions, the metric tensor g_{ij} appears nowhere in the formalism. In fact, for the geometry defined by measurements in the usual way with real rods and clocks, f_{ij} is the metric tensor.[8]

It should be noted also, that because of the universal character of the inertial anisotropy, being present in the same way for all particles (or fields) the spatial anisotropy is unobservable locally. The easiest way to see this is to note that a co-ordinate system can always be chosen in such a way as to cause f_{ij} to be locally Minkowskian with vanishing first derivatives. For this coordinate system, the anisotropy of inertial mass appears explicitly nowhere in the equations.

While, with these assumptions, inertial anisotropy is not locally observable, the fact that the geometry defined by real rods and clocks is non-Euclidean may be interpreted as due in part to the effect on rods and clocks of the anisotropy of the inertial mass of the elementary particles which comprise the rods and clocks.

It is concluded finally that the extremely accurate null result of the experiment of Hughes *et al*, does not cast doubt upon the validity of Mach's principle. On the contrary, and in accordance with the requirements of Mach's principle, this impor-tant experiment shows, with great precision, that inertial anisotropy effects are universal, the same for all particles.

Notes to Appendix I

[1] G. Cocconi and E. E. Salpeter, *Nuovo cimento* **10**, 646 (1958); *Phys. Rev. Letters*, **4**, 176 (1960).

[2] V. W. Hughes, H. G. Robinson, and V. Beltrow-Lopez, *Phys. Rev. Letters*, **4**, 342 (1960).

[3] R. W. P. Drever, *Phil. Mag.*, **6**, 683 (1961).

[4] G. Berkeley, *The Principle of Human Knowledge* (1710), par. 111–117.

[5] E. Mach, *Conservation of Energy* (1872) (edition of Open Court Publishing Company, Chicago, Illinois, 1911), Note No. 1; *Science of Mechanics* (1883) (edition of Open Court Pub-lishing Company, Chicago, Illinois, 1902), Chap. II, Sec. VI.

[6] D. W. Sciama, Monthly Notices Roy. Astron. Soc. **113**, 34 (1953); *The Unity of the Uni-verse* (Doubleday, New York, 1959), Chaps. 7–9.

[7] C. W. Sherwin, H. Frauenfelder, E. L. Garwin, E. Lüscher, S. Margulies, and R. N. Peacock, *Phys. Rev. Letters*, **4**, 399 (1960).

[8] What then is the significance of the redundant tensor g_{ij}? As was discussed recently (C. Brans and R. H. Dicke, *Phys. Rev.*, **124**, 925 (1961)), the choice of units of length and time are arbitrary and physical laws must be invariant under position-dependent transformation of units. As a result, considerable freedom in the definition of the metric tensor exists. While f_{ij} would be the natural and simplest choice, the metric tensor can be modified at will and can be defined as g_{ij} by the appropriate redefinition of units. In particular, there exist definitions of units for which the space is flat, all the Riemannian invariants being zero. (See Appendices 7 and 2.)

Appendix 2
Mach's Principle and Invariance under Transforma-tion of Units*
R. H. Dicke

Reprinted from *The Physical Review*, Vol. 125, No. 6, 2163–2167, March 15, 1962

A gravitational theory compatible with Mach's principle was published recently by Brans and Dicke. It is characterized by a gravitational field of the Jordon type, tensor plus scalar field. It is shown here that a coordinate-dependent transformation of the units of measure can be used to throw the theory into a form for which the gravitational field appears in the conventional form, as a metric tensor, such that the Einstein field equation is satisfied. The scalar field appears then as a "matter field" in the theory. The invariance of physical laws under coordinate-dependent transformations of units is discussed.

* This work was supported by the Office of Naval Research and the U.S. Atomic Energy Commission.

In a recent paper[1], a modified relativistic theory of gravitation, closely related to Jordans' theory[2], was developed, compatible with Mach's principle. It was indicated that the resulting formalism was but one particular representation of the theory, based upon a particular definition of the units of mass, length, and time.

The purposes of this note are, first to discuss very briefly the invariance of physical laws under units transformations[3], and second to give another representation of the above theory, completely equivalent to it and derived from it by a simple transformation of units.

The first representation of the theory[1] could be characterized concisely as a relativity theory for which the gravitational field is described by a metric tensor and a scalar, but for which the equations of motion of matter in a given field are identical with those of General Relativity, not being explicitly dependent upon the scalar field. Because of the inclusion of the auxiliary scalar, as part of the gravitational field, the theory is both formally and in its physical interpretation different from General Relativity. It will be shown that this is only apparent, and that a simple redefinition of units causes the scalar to appear in the theory as a nongravitational field, Einstein's field equations being satisfied.

Invariance Under Transformations of Units

Everyone, including the college freshman, is familiar with the usefulness of dimensional considerations in formulating physical laws. Dimensional analysis is essentially an elementary group theoretic technique applied to the equations of physics. It is evident that the particular values of the units of mass, length, and time employed are arbitrary and that the laws of physics must be invariant under a transformation of units. (The units and dimensions employed need not be three in number, nor need they be limited to the traditional mass, length, and time.)

The invariance which we wish to consider here is broader than the elementary consideration described above. Imagine, if you will, that you are told by a space traveller that a hydrogen atom on Sirius has the same diameter as one on the earth. A few moments' thought will convince you that the statement is either a definition or else meaningless. It is evident that two rods side by side, stationary with respect to each other, can be intercompared and equality established in the sense of an approximate congruence between them. However, this cannot be done for perpendicular rods, for rods moving relatively, or for rods with either a space- or time-like separation. Their intercomparison for purposes of establishing equality cannot be made until rules of correspondence are established.

Generally, there may be more than one feasible way of establishing the equality of units at different spacetime points. It is evident then, that the equations of motion of matter must be invariant under a general coordinate-dependent transformation of units. It should be emphasized that the coordinate system is to be held fixed under a units transformation, whereas under a general coordinate transformation the system of physical units is held fixed but coordinates are varied. Thus, under a general transformation of units, the labeling of the space-time coincidence between two particles (coordinates) is invariant, whereas the scalar curvature and other purely geometrical scalars, invariant under coordinate transformations, are generally not invariant under a transformation of units.

It may be noted, for example, that a units transformation can be used to redefine the Riemannian geometry of general relativity in such a way that the resulting geometry is flat. (See Appendix A.)

We are not concerned here with the problem of the general transformation of units, but rather with one of more limited scope, the transformation of the formalism discussed in Reference 1 under a limited class of units transformations. The transformation to be considered is a simple position-dependent scale factor applied to units of length, time, and reciprocal mass.

The velocity of light is invariant under such a transformation and the local-Lorentz invariance of the theory is preserved. It should be noted that this is not a matter of necessity but rather of convenience.

The unit of action, hence Planck's constant, is also invariant under the transformation. This is a matter of convenience in the sense that the form assumed by the equations of a quantum-mechanical formalism are familiar.

Under this transformation, all three quantities, time, length, and reciprocal mass transform in the same way. Hence we may, if we wish, assign the same dimension, say time, to the three quantities. As mentioned above, it is necessary to interpret the generalized coordinates of a point as fixed labels, invariant under a transformation of units. Then with the assumption that

$$ds = (g_{ij} \, dx^i \, dx^j)^{1/2} \tag{1}$$

has the dimensions of time, g_{ij} transforms like a time squared. If the size of the unit of time is scaled by a dimensionless factor $\lambda^{-1/2}$, an arbitrary function of coordinates, a time interval (i.e., the number of units required to represent the interval) scales as $\lambda^{1/2}$. Also the metric tensor components transform as

$$g_{ij} \to \lambda g_{ij},$$
$$g^{ij} \to \lambda^{-1} g^{ij}. \tag{2}$$

Hence, the transformation of the spatial geometry is *conformal*.

The mass of a particle transforms as

$$m \to \lambda^{-1/2} m. \tag{3}$$

The electronic charge, the velocity of light, Planck's constant, and the electromagnetic four potentials are invariant under the transformation.

While λ may be taken to be an arbitrary function of coordinates, we may also limit ourselves to the case of λ a definite function of the scalar φ, of the Brans–Dicke formalism.[1] By so doing, rules of measure are established, for the scalar φ is locally observable. (It is measured with a φ meter, a black box having a pointer and a scale calibrated in units of MT^2L^{-3}. One type of black box contains a torsion balance deflected by the gravitational field produced by massive weights, held mechanically in fixed positions in the box.) Once φ, hence λ, is measured, the correction factor to be applied locally to a rod or clock is determined.

From a slightly different point of view, a unit of length can be established, in principle, in terms of the diameter of a planetary orbit in a solar system which can be transported (at least in time), alternatively in units of the diameter of the hydrogen atom, or with any combination of these two lengths. These various units are not in a fixed ratio in this theory but vary as functions of φ. It should be noted that it is necessary first to make a choice of the unit of length before a space-time geometry is established.

Mach's Principle, expressed in Transformed Units

In Reference 1 the gravitational coupling constant

$$Gm^2/\hbar c \sim 10^{-40} \tag{4}$$

(m the mass of some elementary particle) was interpreted not as a *fait accompli* presented to us by nature and unrelated to other parts of physics, but rather as a number determined, consistent with the requirements of Mach's principle, by the total mass distribution in the universe. Being a dimensionless number, it is invariant under a transformation of units.

It was emphasized in Reference 1 that the formalism developed there was but a particular representation of the theory, a representation for which $\hbar$, c, and m were constant by definition and for which G was coordinate dependent, being determined by the scalar field φ. This representation had the great advantage that the equations of motion of "matter" in a known and given metric field were identical with those of General Relativity. For example, geodesic equations of motion are obtained for unchanged, zero-spin particles. These advantages are to be balanced against the disadvantage that the description of gravitational interactions is more complex, Einstein's field equation not being valid.

For the particular representation of the theory to be given here, the gravitational constant G, also $\hbar$, and c are constant by definition, and the rest masses of all elementary particles vary with position, being functions of φ, albeit in the same way, the mass ratios of different types of particles being constant.

As was mentioned above, this representation of the theory has the form of a "general relativity," Einstein's field equation being satisfied. The scalar φ of the theory plays the role of still another nongravitational field. If the field exists, its effects have not yet been observed with certainty.

Being a boson field generated by all matter, it is extraordinarily difficult to observe. The effect of nearby matter, in the laboratory, in generating this field is minor in comparison with the dominating influences of the enormously greater amounts of matter in the distant parts of the essentially static universe.

We turn now to the transformation of the formalism of Reference 1 under the above described units transformation. This transformation, conformal in type, is similar to that discussed by Fierz[4] in his analysis of Jordan's theory.[2]

In Reference 1, the equations of motion of matter and the gravitational field equations are derived from the variational principle

$$0 = \delta \int \left[\varphi R - \omega \frac{\varphi_{,i}\varphi^{,i}}{\varphi} + \frac{16\pi}{c^4} L \right] (-g)^{1/2} d^4x, \tag{5}$$

where R is the scalar curvature of the Riemannian space, is the Lagrangian density of matter (i.e., nongravitational fields) and φ is the above-mentioned scalar field, a field to be interpreted as part of the gravitational field which in this theory is described by both g_{ij} and φ. ω is a dimensionless constant of the order of unity. The

8*

Lagrangian density of matter is assumed to be completely standard, the usual scalar of special relativity generalized by replacing the Minkowskian metric tensor η_{ij} by the generally covariant metric tensor g_{ij}.

In order to show explicitly the transformation of the matter Lagrangian density, an example is constructed, for a system of charged particles interacting electromagnetically

$$L = -\frac{1}{(-g)^{1/2}} \sum \int [mc^2(-u^iu_i)^{1/2} + eA_iu^i]\delta^4(x - z)\, d\tau - \frac{1}{16\pi} F^{ij}F_{ij}. \quad (6)$$

Here the sum is over all particles, the particle position z is a function of the proper time τ, and the four-velocity is

$$u^i = dx^i/d\tau, \quad (7)$$

also

$$ds^2 = g_{ij}\, dx^i dx^j = -d\tau^2,$$

$$u^iu_i = -1, \quad (8)$$

$$g_{00} < 0.$$

As usual

$$F_{ij} = A_{i,j} - A_{j,i} \quad (8)$$

Measured in the new units defined above the mass of the particle becomes

$$\bar{m} = \lambda^{-1/2}m, \quad (9a)$$

or

$$m = \lambda^{1/2}\bar{m}.$$

In similar fashion, the other quantities in equation (6) are

$$m = \lambda^{1/2}\bar{m},$$
$$g_{ij} = \lambda^{-1}\bar{g}_{ij},$$
$$g^{ij} = \lambda\bar{g}^{ij},$$
$$d\tau = \lambda^{-1/2}\, d\bar{\tau},$$
$$ds = \lambda^{-1/2}\, d\bar{s},$$
$$(-g)^{1/2} = \lambda^{-2}(-\bar{g})^{1/2},$$
$$u^i = \lambda^{1/2}\bar{u}^i,$$
$$A_i = \bar{A}_i, \quad (10)$$
$$F_{ij} = \bar{F}_{ij},$$
$$F^{ij} = \lambda^2\bar{F}^{ij},$$
$$e = \bar{e},$$
$$c = \bar{c},$$
$$\hbar = \bar{\hbar},$$
$$\delta^4 = \bar{\delta}^4,$$
$$\varphi = \lambda\bar{\varphi}.$$

For completeness φ, which has the dimensions of G^{-1} or $L^{-3}T^{+2}M^{+1} \sim T^{-2}$, is included in the above list. Making the above transformations we have

$$L = \lambda^2 \bar{L}, \tag{11}$$

where L is L measured in the new units, obtained from L by replacing all quantities by bared quantities.

The transformation of the scalar curvature R under a conformal transformation is a well-known problem in Riemannian geometry. The result is[5] that

$$R = \lambda(\bar{R} + 3\square \ln\lambda - \tfrac{3}{2}\lambda^{-2\lambda}{}_{,i}\lambda_{,j}\bar{g}^{ij}), \tag{12}$$

where

$$\square \ln\lambda = \frac{1}{(-\bar{g})^{1/2}}((-\bar{g})^{1/2}\bar{g}^{ij}\lambda^{-1}{}_{,i})^\lambda{}_{,j}. \tag{13}$$

In similar fashion the last term in equation (5) is easily transformed to give

$$\frac{\varphi_{,i}\varphi^{,i}}{\varphi} = \lambda^2, \frac{\bar{\varphi}_{,i}\varphi^{,i}}{\bar{\varphi}} + 2\lambda\lambda_{,i}\bar{\varphi}^{,i} + \bar{\varphi}\lambda_{,i}\lambda^{,i}. \tag{14}$$

Substituting equations (11), (12), and (14) in equation (5) gives

$$0 = \delta \int \left[\bar{\varphi}\bar{R} + 3\bar{\varphi}\square\ln\lambda - \tfrac{1}{2}(3 + 2\omega)\bar{\varphi}\frac{-\lambda_{,i}\lambda^{,i}}{\lambda^2} \right.$$
$$\left. -2\omega\frac{\lambda_{,i}\varphi^{,i}}{\lambda} - \omega\frac{\bar{\varphi}_{,i}\varphi^{,i}}{\bar{\varphi}} + \frac{16\pi}{c^4}\bar{L} \right](-\bar{g})^{1/2}\,d^4x. \tag{15}$$

One should be reminded that λ in equation (15) may be regarded as a known and given function of coordinates, or alternatively as a function of φ. We are interested principally in a choice of λ, a function of φ, that results in $\bar{\varphi}$ being constant. This is

$$\lambda = \varphi/\bar{\varphi}, \tag{16}$$

where $\bar{\varphi}$ is constant, the value of φ at some arbitrarily chosen point. As $\bar{\varphi}$ is now constant, the variational equation becomes, after dropping the ordinary divergence $(-\bar{g})^{1/2}\square\ln\lambda$,

$$0 = \delta \int \left[\bar{R} - \tfrac{1}{2}(2\omega + 3)\frac{\lambda_{,i}\lambda^{,i}}{\lambda^2} + \frac{16\pi}{c^4\bar{\varphi}}\bar{L} \right](-\bar{g})^{1/2}\,d^4x. \tag{17}$$

λ must now be considered a dynamic variable, and it must be varied in equation (17). In addition to the above second term, λ occurs explicitly only in $\bar{m} = m\lambda^{-1/2}$, ($m$ constant).

To cast this variational principle in a form completely familiar, write

$$0 = \delta \int \left[\bar{R} + \frac{16\pi G_0}{c^4}(\bar{L} + \bar{L}_\lambda) \right](-\bar{g})^{1/2}\,d^4x, \tag{18}$$

with $G_0 = \bar{\varphi}^{-1}$ and

$$\bar{L}_\lambda = -\frac{(3 + 2\omega)c^4\lambda_{,i}\lambda^{,i}}{32\pi G_0\lambda^2}. \tag{19}$$

Now λ is to be considered a "matter field" and the total Lagrangian density of "matter" is $\bar{L} + \bar{L}_\lambda$. Varying $\bar{g}_{ij}$ in equation (18) gives Einstein's field equations

$$\bar{R}^{ij} - \tfrac{1}{2}\bar{g}^{ij}\bar{R} = \frac{8\pi G_0}{c^4}\bar{\mathfrak{T}}^{ij}, \tag{20}$$

where

$$\bar{\mathfrak{T}}^{ij} = \bar{T}^{ij} + \bar{\Lambda}^{ij} = \frac{2}{(-\bar{g})^{1/2}}\frac{\partial}{\partial\bar{g}_{ij}}[(-\bar{g})^{1/2}(\bar{L} + \bar{L}_\lambda)] \tag{21}$$

is the energy-momentum tensor of matter. It satisfies the local conservation relation

$$(\bar{\mathfrak{T}}^{ij})_{;j} = 0. \tag{22}$$

Varying equation (17) with respect to λ gives

$$\overline{\square}(\ln\lambda) = -\frac{16\pi}{(2\omega + 3)\bar{\varphi}c^4}\lambda\frac{\partial L}{\partial\lambda} = \frac{8\pi}{\bar{\varphi}c^4(3 + 2\omega)}\bar{T}, \tag{23}$$

with

$$\bar{T} = \bar{T}_i{}^i = \bar{g}_{ij}\frac{2}{(-\bar{g})^{1/2}}\frac{\partial}{\partial\bar{g}_{ij}}((-\bar{g})^{1/2}\bar{L}). \tag{24}$$

The second equality of equation (23) follows explicitly from the form of equation (6) If the transformation relation

$$\bar{T} = \lambda^{-2}T \tag{25}$$

is substituted in equation (24), one obtains

$$\square\lambda = \frac{8\pi}{\bar{\varphi}c^4(3 + 2\omega)}T, \tag{26}$$

which is equivalent to equation (13) of Reference (1).

While the representation of the theory used here has certain advantages over that of Reference 1, it is clumsy in some ways. For example, freely falling matter does not move on geodesics of the geometry, although light rays still follow null geodesics. Also, the measures provided by rods and clocks are not invariant in this geometry. For example, in this formalism the gravitational red shift appears only partially as a metric phenomenon, the remainder of the effect being described as due to a "real" change in the energy levels of an atom with λ.

Consider the motion of an unchanged spinless particle in the gravitational field. The equations of motion obtained from the variational principle, equation (15), are

$$\frac{d}{d\bar{\tau}}(\bar{m}\bar{g}_{ij}\bar{u}^j) - \tfrac{1}{2}\bar{m}\bar{g}_{jk,i}\bar{u}^j\bar{u}^k + \bar{m}_{,i} = 0. \tag{27}$$

The last term represents a nongravitational force and results in a nongeodesic motion of the particle. The inverse of the units transformation applied to equation (27) gives the expected geodesic equation of the old geometry

$$\frac{d}{d\tau}(mg_{ij}u^j) - \tfrac{1}{2}mg_{jk,i}u^ju^k = 0. \tag{28}$$

Note that the gravitational constant measured by a Cavendish experiment would not be G_0 of equation (20) as it does not include the effect of the "nongravitational" interaction with the λ field.

While dimensionless arguments were used above to obtain the λ dependence of inertial mass, the existence of such a dependence is a consequence of dynamical considerations and is not a separate assumption. Quite generally, the mass of a particle varies, being a function of the potential, if it interacts with a scalar field. This can be seen by starting with the variation principle

$$0 = \delta \int [m(-\bar{u}^i \bar{u}_i)^{1/2} + m\psi]\, d\tau, \tag{29}$$

where $m\psi$ is the scalar potential and the mass m is assumed to be constant. The variations in equation (29) may not be taken arbitrarily but must be subject to the constraint

$$\bar{u}^i \bar{u}_i = -1. \tag{30}$$

The resulting equation of motion is identical with equation (27) with

$$\overline{m} = m\psi. \tag{31}$$

If the variational equation is taken as

$$0 = \delta \int \overline{m}(-\bar{u}^i \bar{u}_i)^{1/2}\, d\bar{\tau}. \tag{32}$$

The same equation of motion is obtained, as the Euler equation, without the necessity for introducing the constraint explicitly.

Summary and Conclusion

The field equations compatible with Mach's principle which were previously formulated,[1] are here transformed in such a way that the required modification appears as part of the nongravitational field, Einstein's field equations being valid. The rest masses of all particles are affected by an interaction with a scalar field. This interaction reduces the masses of the particles and the gravitational coupling constant, equation (4), may be interpreted as small because the particle mass m is reduced drastically by interaction with the field, generated by the enormous amounts of matter in the universe.

In similar fashion the relation[6]

$$GM/Rc^2 \sim 1 \tag{33}$$

is understandable. (M is the mass of the universe out to visible limits, and R, the Hubble radius, is a measure of the radius of this visible portion.) Measured in the new units, the masses of elementary particles adjust themselves, through the scalar field generated by all the other matter, in such a way that the ratio M/R stays constant and of the order of magnitude of $G^{-1}c^2$.[1]

Appendix A

Transformation of the metric of a Riemannian space to that of a flat space. As a first step a coordinate system, time orthogonal, is chosen. This can be done, at least for a finite coordinate patch, by erecting a family of geodesic curves normal to any space-like surface and using it to define a second space-like surface everywhere equidistant from the first. Corresponding points on the two surfaces, labeled by the same space-like coordinates x^1, x^2, x^3, are points joined by the same normal geodesic curve. The time coordinate is assigned different values on each of the two surfaces. The procedure can be iterated to assign coordinates to all points in the coordinate patch.

Let g_{ij} be the metric tensor in a particular time orthogonal coordinate system. Then

$$g_{0\alpha} = 0, \qquad \alpha = 1, 2, 3. \tag{34}$$

Introduce the tensor $T_i{}^j$ having the inverse $\tilde{T}_i{}^j$

$$T_i{}^j \tilde{T}_j{}^k = \delta_i{}^k, \tag{35}$$

such that for *this particular coordinate system* the tensor (interpreted as a matrix) is orthogonal,

$$T_i{}^j = \tilde{T}_j{}^i. \tag{36}$$

It is a well-known theorem of matrix algebra that any symmetric matrix can be diagonalized by an orthogonal transformation. Hence, it is always possible to so choose $T_i{}^j$ that

$$T_k{}^i g_{ij} T_l{}^j = \bar{g}_{kl}, \tag{37}$$

with $\bar{g}_{ki}$ purely diagonal in this coordinate system.

Corresponding to the coordinate intervals dx^i, one can define new intervals through the transformation

$$d\bar{x}^i = \tilde{T}_j{}^i \, dx^j. \tag{38}$$

It must be emphasized that this transformation does not generally represent a coordinate transformation.

The infinitesimal separation of two neighboring points is ds with

$$ds^2 = g_{ij} \, dx^i \, dx^j. \tag{39}$$

This can now be given as

$$ds^2 = g_{ij} T_m{}^i T_n{}^j \tilde{T}_k{}^m \tilde{T}_l{}^n \, dx^k \, dx^l = \bar{g}_{ij} \, d\bar{x}^i \, d\bar{x}^j. \tag{40}$$

As g_{ij} is diagonal, the intervals $d\bar{x}^i$ are all mutually orthogonal. Now by redefining the measure of time, and of length along the three mutually perpendicular space-like directions $d\bar{x}^\alpha$, $\bar{g}_{ij}$ can be transformed into any other diagonal tensor of the same signature. In particular, it can be transformed into the Minkowskian metric tensor η_{ij}. The resulting measure of interval between the two points is

$$d\bar{s}^2 = \eta_{ij} \, d\bar{x}^i \, d\bar{x}^j. \tag{41}$$

Because the original coordinate system was time orthogonal, the orthogonal transformation

$$d\bar{x}^i = \tilde{T}_j{}^i \, dx^j \tag{42}$$

represents a space-like local rotation, hence the Minkowskian tensor η_{ij} is invariant under this transformation. Consequently,

$$d\bar{s}^2 = \eta_{ij} \, d\bar{x}^i \, d\bar{x}^j = \eta_{ij} \, dx^i \, dx^j. \tag{43}$$

Note that equation (43) gives a new measure of interval and a *new metric tensor* for the *old coordinate system*.

The new measure of interval leads to a flat space with a Minkowskian metric tensor. It should be noted that the transformed coordinate intervals are mutually orthogonal both before and after units are redefined. Hence, the criteria for orthogonality of these vectors are independent of units and the condition of local orthogonality may be meaningfully imposed.

Null geodesics are generally *not* invariant under this transformation of units. The velocity of light varies, being a function of both coordinates and spatial directions. Physically, with the redefined units, space might be considered to have some of the electromagnetic properties of an anisotropic medium. However, these properties can be eliminated by a units transformation and they are without a physical significance, invariant under this group. It should be noted that the same objection, based on considerations of invariance under units transformations, can be leveled against the reading of physical significance into the geometrical invariants. These "invariants", such as the scalar curvature, are not invariant under a units transformation.

Because of the various nonequivalent ways of establishing standards of mass, length, and time within the framework of the Brans–Dicke theory, invariance under the units transformation group is particularly important. This is of lesser importance in standard general relativity. However, even here it is possible, in principle, to construct rods and clocks whose units are dependent upon some scalar field variable such as a curvature "invariant" or a Maxwell invariant.

Notes and References to Appendix 2

[1] C. Brans and R. H. Dicke, *Phys. Rev.* **124** (1961). (see appendix 7).

[2] P. Jordan, *Schwerkraft und Weltall* (Friedrick Viewig und Sohn, Braunschweig, 1955).

[3] Alternative systems of units seem to have been first introduced into relativity by E. A. Milne [*Kinematic Relativity* (Oxford University Press, New York, 1948)]. Systematic discussions of units transformations were introduced by A. G. Walker [*Proc. Roy. Soc. Edinburgh*, **62**, 164 (1946)] and by G. C. McVittie [*Proc. Roy. Soc. Edinburgh*, **62**, 147 (1945)]. More recently a discussion of conformal units transformations has been given by H. Nariai and Y. Ueno [*Progr. Theoret. Phys.* (Kyoto) **24**, 593 (1960)].
See also Hoffmann, P.R. **89**, 52 (1953).

[4] M. Fierz, *Helv. Phys. Acta*, **29**, 128 (1956); see also the discussion by P. Jordan, Reference 2, and *Z. Physik*, **157**, 112 (1959); O. Heckmann, *Z. Astrophys*, **40**, 278 (1956), and the summary in D. R. Brill's article, Varenna summer school notes. 1961 (unpublished).

[5] J. L. Synge, *Relativity, The General Theory* (North-Holland Publishing Company, Amsterdam, 1960), p. 318.

[6] D. W. Sciama, *Monthly Notices Roy. Astron. Soc.*, **113**, 34 (1953); R. H. Dicke, *Am. Scientist*, **47**, 25 (1959); R. H. Dicke, *Science*, **129**, 621 (1959).

Appendix 3

Long-range Scalar Interaction*

R. H. Dicke

Reprinted from *The Physical Review*, Vol. 126, No. 5, 1875–1877, June 1, 1962

The long-range scalar field, associated with a neutral, massless, boson, has been generally considered to be nonexistent. This belief is based on the lack of overt effects, observed in the laboratory, from such a field. It is shown that if this long-range interaction were to exist, it would of necessity be weak. The physical reason for this is the large contribution, having its origin in the enormous amount of matter at great distance in the universe, to the magnitude of the scalar. By comparison, the contribution of local matter is miniscule, leading to a weak interaction of about the same strength as gravitation. Further more, it is shown that such an interaction, in its effects, would be very similar to gravitation and could be distinguished only with difficulty. It is concluded that there is not yet a compelling observation which could be used to exclude the long-range scalar interaction.

The neutral, massless, boson fields play a uniquely important role in the universe. They are the sources of the quasi-static long-range interactions by which distant parts of the universe make their presence felt in the laboratory. If it be assumed that nature abhors a field more complicated than tensor, i.e., an elementary particle spin greater than 2, then only three types of fields require consideration, scalar, vector, and tensor.

Examples of vector and tensor fields are known, in the form of electromagnetism and gravitation. While electromagnetism apparently plays an important role in the dynamics of the galaxy, there is little reason to believe that, aside from radiation effects it is important for cosmology. In fact, with the usual assumption that the universe is uniform and isotropic when averaged over large volumes, the average electric charge density must be zero, for the isotropy of space requires the vanishing of electric and magnetic fields, implying in turn the vanishing of average charge and current densities.

The metric tensor field associated with inertial and gravitational forces is presumably an instrument through which the mass distribution of the universe makes its presence felt in the laboratory. It is presumed that, in accordance with Mach's Principle, the local inertia coordinate systems are determined by the mass distribution of the universe. However, the appropriate boundary conditions upon the metric field, which would exhibit generally this unique dependence upon the mass distribution, have not yet been formulated. According to general relativity this is the sole local influence of distant matter, and, in accordance with the equivalence principle, in a freely falling, nonrotating laboratory there are no observable gravitational effects having their origin in distant matter (aside from, generally weak, tidal effects).

If one were to have some small faith in the proposition that nature is not capricious, that the physical world is ultimately simple, then the simplest of the three fields, the scalar field, might be expected to exist and to play an important role in the universe. However, it is generally believed to be missing. The basis for this

* This research was, in part, supported by the U.S. Atomic Energy Commission and the Office of Naval Research.

belief is the lack of any indication in laboratory experiments of such a scalar interaction.

While, the scalar interaction might be so weak as to be undetectable, this is generally considered unlikely, for gravitation is the only extremely weak interaction known. Apparently strong interactions (and moderately weak interactions) are much more common than the extremely weak. Also, it is argued that the interaction would need to be excessively weak, even when compared with gravitation, or it would appear as a gravitational anomaly in the Eötvös experiment and as an anomaly in the motions of the planets.

It is the purpose of this note to point out that both of these assumptions are incorrect, that the scalar interaction, if it exists, is expected to be very weak, and, with assumption discussed in paragraph (3) below, that the scalar interaction masquerades like gravitation, being almost indistinguishable from true gravitation.

The long-range scalar interaction (neutral, massless, scalar field) has been discussed by Bergmann,[1] in curved space as part of the gravitational field by Jordan[2] and others,[3–5] and as a matter field in curved space by Dicke.[6] The most important properties of a scalar interaction are summarized here:

(1) If a scalar field φ interacts with a particle, the particle's mass is a function of the scalar.

(2). The equations of motion of a particle in a gravitational and a scalar field are

$$(d/d\tau)(mu_i) - \tfrac{1}{2}mg_{jk,i}u^j u^k + (dm/d\varphi)\varphi_{,i} = 0. \tag{1}$$

(3) To avoid difficulties with the Eötvös experiment, one must assume a common functional dependence upon φ for all elementary particles, $m = m_0 f(\varphi)$, with f the same for all particles.

(4) Equation (1) is obtained from the variational principle,

$$0 = \delta \int m(-g_{ij}u^i u^j)^{1/2}\, d\tau. \tag{2}$$

However the factor f can be taken under the integral sign and combined with g_{ij} to define a new metric tensor $\bar{g}_{ij} = f^2 g_{ij}$. Thus, the scalar interaction can be combined with the tensor interaction to give a new effective gravitational interaction, associated with a new metric tensor. The scalar interaction no longer appears explicitly.

(5) The source strength of a body for the generation of a scalar field is given by an integral over the body of the contracted energy-momentum tensor of matter. Because of the virial theorem, and for a stationary body, this is equal, when time averaged, to the negative of the mass of the body. Thus, for those cases where experimental tests exist, both the scalar and gravitational fields are proportional to the same parameter, the mass of the source.

As a result of propositions (3) and (4) above, it is clear that the effect of a given scalar field, externally produced, is indistinguishable from the gravitational field. (This, however, does not mean that there are no observable effects of a scalar field. For example, a light ray is not deflected by a scalar interaction, and the expected perihelion rotation of Mercury may be noticably different[5] from the general relativity value. The radial dependence of $\bar{g}_{ij}$ for the Schwarzschild solution is different from the usual result of general relativity.)

One question remains: Why should the scalar interaction be so weak? We shall show that, if it exists, the scalar interaction would be expected to have a strength of the order of magnitude of the normal gravitational interaction.

It will be assumed that $f(\varphi)$ can be approximated by a power dependence $f \cong a\varphi^{-n}$ when φ falls in a sufficiently narrow range. The wave equation satisfied by φ is then[5,6]

$$\Box \varphi = \frac{1}{(-g)^{1/2}}[(-g)^{1/2}\varphi^{,i}]_{,i} = \frac{n}{\varphi}T, \tag{3}$$

where n is a constant and T is the contracted energy momentum tensor of matter. If a function of φ were to appear inside the d'Alembertian operator, the scalar φ could be redefined to eliminate it.

For a static configuration of astronomical bodies of mass m_i, equation (3) has an approximate solution:

$$\varphi \cong \frac{n}{4\pi} \sum \frac{m_i c^2}{\varphi_i r_i}. \tag{4}$$

In equation (4) it is assumed that the curvature of the space is sufficiently small that a Minkowskian coordinate system can be used, at least over a limited region; r_i is radial distance in this coordinate system.

It is evident that as the sum in equation (4) is extended over larger and larger regions, the neglect of the radial expansion of the universe and the non-Euclidean character of space becomes increasingly intolerable. It would be physically reasonable to expect that, for purposes of an order of magnitude calculation, the sum in equation (4) could be cut off at the Hubble radius, the farthest extent of the visible universe. This conclusion has been justified quantitatively, for a particular cosmological model. Assuming outgoing-wave boundary conditions on φ, essentially this result in equation (4) has been obtained by expressing the solution in terms of a Green's function.[5]

Thus, for the spatial dependencies of φ about a local body, such as the sun, one can write.

$$\varphi \cong \frac{n}{4\pi\varphi_0} \frac{m_s c^2}{r} + \varphi_0, \tag{5}$$

with

$$\varphi_0 \sim \frac{n}{4\pi\varphi_0} \int_0^R \frac{\rho c^2}{r} 4\pi r^2 \, dr = \frac{n}{\varphi_0} \frac{R^2}{2}\rho c^2. \tag{6}$$

Equation (6) is a crude approximation only. ρ is the mean matter density of the universe and R is the Hubble radius. With the observed mass density,

$$G\rho R^2/c^2 \sim 1, \tag{7}$$

and equation (6) can be written

$$\varphi_0 \sim (n/G)^{1/2}c^2. \tag{8}$$

From equation (1) the scalar interaction force produced by the sun on a nearby body of mass m is

$$F = c^2\frac{dm}{d\varphi} \frac{d\varphi}{dr} = -c^2 nm\frac{1}{\varphi} \frac{d\varphi}{dr} = n^2\frac{mm_s c^4}{4\pi\varphi_0^2 r^2} = (n/4\pi)(Gmm_s/r^2). \tag{9}$$

Because of the crude order of magnitude nature of equations (6) and (7), the factor n in equation (9) is not significant. All that can be asserted is that the scalar interaction strength is of the same rough order of magnitude as gravitation. It could differ by at least a factor of 10.

To summarize, it is concluded that the absence of overt effects, observed in the laboratory, due to a longrange scalar field does not imply the nonexistence of the field. The effect of nearby matter in generating this scalar is minuscule compared with the dominant effect of the enormous amounts of matter in distant parts of the universe. As a result the scalar interaction is very weak. A further complication is introduced by the fact that the scalar field masquerades as gravitation and can be distinguished from gravitation only with difficulty. The difficulties in observing the effects of such a weak scalar field have been discussed[7,8]. These difficulties are sufficiently great that a conclusive test for the scalar field has never been applied. To assert that the scalar field does not exist because it is unobserved is analogous to the claim of a blind man that light does not exist. While the effects of the scalar field could be observed only with difficulty, the question of the existence of the field is of considerable interest. In particular, if this field exists, the great weakness of the gravitational interaction becomes understandable. The extremely small value of the gravitational coupling constant $(Gm_e{}^2/\hbar c \sim 10^{-40})$ is then recognized as the effect of the enormous amount of matter in the universe generating a scalar field which acts to depress the value of m_e, the mass of an elementary particle.

Notes and References to Appendix 3

[1] P. G. Bergmann, *Am. J. Phys.*, **24**, 38 (1956).

[2] P. Jordan, *Schwerkraft und Weltall* (Friedrich Viewig und Sohn, Braunschweig, 1955).

[3] G. Ludwig, *Fortschritte der projektiven Relativitätstheorie* (Friedrich Vieweg und Sohn, Braunschweig, 1951).

[4] K. Just, *Z. Physik*, **140**, 485 (1955).

[5] C. Brans and R. H. Dicke, *Phys. Rev.*, **123**, 925 (1961) (see appendix 7).

[6] R. H. Dicke, *Phys. Rev.*, **125**, 2163 (1962) (see appendix 2).

[7] R. H. Dicke, Varenna summer school notes, 1961 (to be published).

[8] R. H. Dicke, *Revs. Modern Phys.*, **34**, 110 (1962) (see appendix 10).

Appendix 4

Field Theories of Gravitation

R. H. Dicke

Two things about gravitation strike the novice as strange. One is the great weakness of the interaction; the other is the interpretation as a manifestation of Riemannian geometry. It is truly remarkable that all other forces are treated as the effects of particle interactions, or when many Bosons are involved as the effect of classical fields, and only gravitation is singled out for the honor of geometrical interpretation.

It is known from the work of Rosen[10], Gupta[11], Feynman[12], Thirring [13] and others that gravitation can be treated as a field within the formal framework of Lorentz invariant theory, but these treatments are only formal, the metric tensor of the Minkowski metric being unobservable.

It is also known that there is a large element of arbitrariness in the definition of the geometry of space and that the particular definition employed in general relativity is in no sense unique. It is helpful in this connection to remember that "geometry" is a two-part word. It refers not only to a property of the space but equally to the means of measure employed. It is possible to devise many other (ugly) definitions of the metric tensor beside the one employed. A particularly interesting sub-class of units transformations, leading to a redefinition of the metric tensor, is the group of conformal transformations induced by a coordinate dependent scale factor applied to the units of length, time, and reciprocal mass.[15] The conformal factor need not be an arbitrary function of position but may be any function of a field invariant (observable), such as the Maxwell invariant. Thus the new geometry may be so defined that measurements are to be carried out in accordance with the requirements of some simple rule. It is remarkable that although the arbitrariness in the choice of coordinate system is recognized by writing generally covariant equations, the corresponding arbitrariness in units of measure is not recognized by a corresponding covariance.

On the other hand, it can be argued with considerable force that in any case the Riemannian geometry is superfluous and can always be grafted on to the theoretical formalism after the dynamical problem is solved. From this point of view, after a system of coordinates (arbitrary) is chosen and equations of motion for the dynamical variables are written and solved, one has a complete solution to the dynamical problem, and it is only of secondary interest to inquire about the curvature invariant as measured in a particular way. It should be noted that the word "invariant" here is something of a misnomer as the curvature scalar is invariant under coordinate transformations but not under units-transformations.

The types of field theories of gravitation which we would like to consider are those for which the only geometrical concepts introduced *a priori* are those of a differentiable 4-dimensional manifold with neither a metric nor affine connection defined. One would hope to find metrical properties after the dynamical problem is solved.

It should be emphasized that this approach to gravitation as a field theory is very different from the various Lorentz invariant theories of the past. The hope here is not to exhibit a unique theory but rather to construct a large class of possible theories and to have recourse to experimental and observational results to limit the class as much as possible. If after satisfying the various observational requirements the class of possible theories is still very large, one may regard all these theories as possible or else impose requirements of elegance, simplicity, beauty, or some other esthetic consideration.

Fortunately, it will appear that the requirements imposed by observations are sufficiently severe that the class of possible theories is quite small.

It would be impossible to proceed with the program of constructing a large class of possible field theories if one imposed no conditions *a priori*, conditions derived from physical pictures, or conditions philosophical in origin.

The philosophy and the picture that I shall paint as a guide to constructing a formalism need not be accepted, for the same formalism could presumably be obtained in other ways. None the less, I shall give my own personal picture in case the reader might not like to supply his own.

To me the geometry of a physical space is primarily a subjective concept. What is objective is the material content of the space, the photons, electrons, pions, neutrinos, protons, etc., and *gravitons*. I give emphasis to the idea, not yet substantiated by observations, that in the same sense that electromagnetic forces are induced by interactions with photons, gravitational effects are due to collisions with gravitons. I here use the word "graviton" in a generic sense to mean any type of particle responsible for the effect of gravitation. Perhaps it would be better to reserve the word to mean a particular spin two particle and to use other words for other parts of the gravitational field, if other parts should be found.

When particles are present, it becomes possible to add objective elements to the geometrical concepts. Thus, the collision between two particles can be used as a definition of a space-time point. Such an event could be labeled by coordinates, arbitrarily chosen. If particles were present in large numbers, for example, as virtual photons and gravitons, collisions with a test particle (e.g., electron) could be so numerous as to define an almost continuous trajectory.

It is not necessary that one have a physical definition of all the points in our 4-dimensional space. We are familiar with the necessity of employing in physics elements not directly observable, such as the wave function. However, from the point of view of Mach's Principle, the geometrical concepts become completely subjective in the absence of a physical definition of a point. Thus, matter is needed to introduce an objective content into geometry. Also inherent in this idea is the thought that the only physically meaningful position relations are those of matter relative to other matter. The empty background space, of which one's knowledge is only subjective, imposes no dynamical conditions on matter. This idea, due to Bishop Berkeley (1710) and to Mach (1870) strongly suggests that the dynamical equations of physics be generally covariant, for if any particular coordinate system were to be chosen *a priori*, this would generally impose conditions *a priori* on the dynamical problem. Stated physically, the equations of motion would contain arbitrary subjective elements reflecting one's view of the nature of a purely empty, hence unobservable, space. It is to avoid this calamity that one writes generally covariant equations. But is this sufficient? The answer is an unqualified no! If one were to introduce subjective geometrical concepts in a generally covariant way, this would be just as dangerous. For example, one could make the assumption that space is flat and introduce in a generally covariant way the metric tensor of a flat space, *a priori*. If this is done, it is easy to construct meaningless generally covariant equations containing explicitly this arbitrary element. It can be remarked parenthetically that the various flat space theories of gravitation, for which the gravitation is described as a tensor field in flat space, are so contrived as to make the subjective η_{ij} metric tensor disappear as a separate entity.

As discussed above, the definition of a metric is in any case arbitrary, and the safest way to avoid the introduction of a subjective element at this point is to ignore the problem of metrical measure until all dynamical problems are solved. After this, one can introduce any definition of the metric one likes without harming the equations of motion. Thus, the only geometrical elements that we would admit initially are those of a four-dimensional differentiable manifold, with neither metric nor affine connection.

As for dynamical equations, we require that they be derived from an invariant variational principle. It is not easy to justify this strong requirement, but it can be remarked that having the requirements of quantum mechanics in mind and knowing the close connection between wave propagation and an action principle, we are lead to this assumption. Secondly, there is a close connection between variational principles and conservation laws.

In considering dynamical equations, particles will be considered classically or, if large collections of Bosons are involved, as classical fields. It will be assumed that a large collection of particles of a given type can be characterized in its interactions with other fields, or with test particles, by some tensor quantity, never a tensor density.

We will make one final assumption, one which cannot be easily justified. Nature abhors a complicated situation. It will be assumed that if a linear super-position of interactions is possible it will occur in preference to a non-linear one; that an interaction involving but one field will occur before one involving two or more.

Before proceeding, these assumptions will be listed:

(1) Geometrical points are to be associated with physical events.
(2) The only geometrical properties of space introduced *a priori* are those of a 4-dimensional space with an arbitrary coordinate system varying sufficiently smoothly to characterize a differentiable manifold. There shall be neither a metric nor affine connection.
(3) Space will be assumed to have no intrinsic properties (objective) beyond those of the matter contained in the space. The dynamical equations will be constructed in generally covariant form, and they will contain no elements referring to the space except the arbitrary coordinate system (where the coordinates refer to physical events).
(4) Dynamical equations will be obtained from an invariant action principle.
(5) Large numbers of Bosons of the same kind can be characterized in their interaction by a tensor (ie. a scalar, vector, or tensor field).
(6) Nature like things as simple as possible.

Gravitational effects require one or more long-range fields, and we shall assume that these fields are to be associated with clouds of Bosons. We shall want to consider scalar, vector, tensor, and possibly even higher rank tensors and shall ignore spinor fields and fields in the form of densities of various ranks.

As the simplest dynamical problem which we can consider we will imagine a cloud of Bosons interacting only with itself. First, consider the possibility of the cloud being scalarons. This can be excluded, as we could not construct an action principle in the form

$$0 = \delta \int L \, d^4x \tag{1}$$

in which L is a scalar density involving only φ, its derivatives, and elemental tensors and densities $\delta_i{}^j$ and ϵ^{ijkl}.

In considering vector fields, contravariant and covariant vectors must be considered separately, as there is no procedure for lowering or raising indices. A variational principle for a covariant field only can be constructed as

$$0 = \delta \int \epsilon^{ijkl} F_{ij} F_{kl} \, d^4x \tag{2}$$

with

$$F_{ij} = A_{i,j} - A_{j,i}. \tag{3}$$

The resulting Euler equation is linear and could not represent a field interacting with itself (i.e., a swarm of vectorons colliding with each other). The equation is

$$\epsilon^{ijkl}F_{ij,k} = 0 \tag{4}$$

and is satisfied identically for any field A_i. At first glance it would seem that this is a nonsensical result, but it should be remembered that the coordinate system is arbitrary and that it is possible to impose 4 coordinate conditions. These might be taken to be such as to give A_i almost any arbitrary form.

The next dynamical problem to be considered is that of a tensor field interacting with itself. Symmetric covariant and contravariant tensors are not regarded as different as the one can generate the other as a reciprocal. A covariant antisymmetric tensor field will be treated as the curl of a vector field. The symmetric tensor g_{ij} permits the rather uninteresting variational equation

$$0 = \delta \int \sqrt{\pm g}\, d^4x \tag{5}$$

for which the Euler equation requires the vanishing of the field. The plus or minus sign is chosen to make the radical real. At this stage we leave open the possibility that the signature of g_{ij} could be either plus or minus.

We cannot construct an interesting variational equation for gravitons interacting with themselves without introducing derivatives of the field components, and it is necessary to go to 2nd derivatives as all first derivatives can be reduced to zero at any one point by a coordinate transformation.

It is possible to construct 14 algebraically independent scalars from g_{ij}, its reciprocal, and their 1st and 2nd derivatives. We now have an embarrassment of riches. But all of these scalars except one contain 2nd derivatives non-linearly and lead to Euler's equations with 3rd derivatives. The scalar curvature (for our purposes the name is a misnomer) is the unique choice for which the 2nd derivatives are contained linearly and for which they may be removed from the variational equation as a divergence. Making use of the postulate of simplicity we would take this action principle to be

$$0 = \delta \int R\sqrt{\pm g}\, d^4x. \tag{6}$$

The resulting Euler equation is non-linear, is the Einstein matter free field equation and properly represents a tensor field interacting with itself. For simplicity we ignore the possibility of a higher rank tensor field interacting with itself and proceed to the next problem, two interacting fields.

Consider first the scalar field. We can find at least two Lagrangian densities (scalar density) which would represent a scalar field interacting with a vector field alone. They are:

$$\varphi^2 \epsilon^{ijkl}F_{ij}F_{kl} \text{ and } \varphi \epsilon^{ijkl}F_{ij}A_k\varphi_{,l}. \tag{7}$$

As there is no self-interaction possible for the fields φ and A_i, the Euler equations for each of the two fields must be linear in that field (generally inhomogeneous) but not necessarily in the other. Physically this means that for any vector field, assumed to be known and given, the equation of motion of φ must be linear or else scalarons would not be linearily superposable, implying an interaction with each other. This linearity requirement implies that the Lagrangian density is quadratic in each of these fields leading to the unique form given by equation (7). We shall use the first form, keeping in mind that the other is possible.

It must be said that this linearity requirement is not a strong condition as one could conceive of 3-body interactions in which a self-interaction of a field could take place only in the presence of a 2nd field, e.g., two scalarons could collide only in the presence of a vectoron. However, simplicity requires that we ignore such possibilities in the first approximation.

As we have a self-interaction term for neither the scalar nor vector field, we must take the simplest form of action principle containing all the essential elements to be that with the first of equation (7) as the Lagrangian density. This leads to the Euler equations.

$$\varphi \epsilon^{ijkl} F_{ij} F_{kl} = 0 \qquad (8)$$

$$\varphi \varphi_{,k} \epsilon^{ijkl} F_{ij} = 0. \qquad (9)$$

These are five equations for the five unknowns φ, A_i. However, because of the arbitrary coordinate system, four identities are satisfied by these equations, with only one equation remaining as nonredundant.

A theory closer to the physical world as it actually exists can be constructed by considering the scalar field to interact with a tensor field only. The requirement of linearity limits us to two forms quadratic in φ: φ^2 and $\varphi_{,i} \varphi_{,j} g^{ij}$. There is no linearity condition on g_{ij} as it has a self-interaction. Some of the various possible interaction terms, quadratic in φ, in order of increasing complexity are

$$\varphi^2 \sqrt{\pm g}, \quad g^{ij} \varphi_{,i} \varphi_{,j} \sqrt{\pm g}, \quad \varphi^2 R \sqrt{\pm g}, \quad g^{ij} \varphi_{,i} \varphi_{,j} R \sqrt{\pm g}. \qquad (10)$$

Also the set of four terms obtained by dividing by φ are possible, for the Euler equation may be linear but inhomogeneous in φ. A possible variational equation might be constructed by incorporating all of these terms linearly with the tensor self-interaction terms $\sqrt{\pm g}$ and $R \sqrt{\pm g}$.

It is necessary to say a brief word about the terms linear in φ in the Lagrangian density. These lead to terms, in the Euler equation for φ, independent of φ and can be considered physically as representing sources of the scalar field. If such terms were not present, the φ field would be without direct sources.

This is the situation when we consider a vector field interacting with a tensor field only. These are two simple forms quadratic in A_i but non-linear. They are

$$g^{ij} g^{kl} F_{ik} F_{jl} \sqrt{\pm g} \text{ and } g^{ij} A_i A_j \sqrt{\pm g}. \qquad (11)$$

Again more complicated terms can be produced by including R as a factor. In order to incorporate a source term for A_i, it is necessary to introduce a complex coupling such as

$$g^{ij} A_i R_{,j} \sqrt{\pm g}. \qquad (12)$$

Thus far we have considered only fields for which scalars, vectors, and tensors represented the physical properties of swarms of Bosons of various types. We consider now the interaction of such a swarm with a classical particle. It is convenient to introduce an extra geometrical idea in formulating variational equations. The trajectory of the particle in 4-space will be parameterized by a monotonic scalar arbitrarily chosen. By requiring that this parameter transform like a scalar, general covariance is preserved. By requiring that it be otherwise arbitrary, a metrical measure is avoided.

The variational equation for a particle interacting with a known and given field will be assumed to be of the form

$$0 = \delta \int L \partial \chi \tag{13}$$

where χ is the arbitrary parameter.

The introduction of the path parameter χ enables the definition of a generalized 4-velocity for the particle

$$u^i = \frac{d\chi^i}{d\chi}. \tag{14}$$

A particle cannot interact with a scalar field alone, as there is no invariant that can be constructed from φ and u^i except $\varphi_{,i} u^i$ such that the integral (13) is independent of a variation of the arbitrary χ. This later requirement is necessary if the Euler equations are to describe a trajectory which is not conditioned by the choice of χ. On the other hand, $\varphi_{,i} u^i$ does not yield a meaningful variational equation as it is a total derivative of φ with respect to χ and contributes to the value of the integral only at the end points.

The Lagrangians for interactions with vector and tensor fields are respectively the unique forms of $A_i u^i$ and $\sqrt{\pm g_{ij} u^i u^j}$. It should be noted that these are the only possible interactions with single fields of these types.

Joint interactions with two fields are represented by the terms

$$\varphi A_i u^i, \quad \varphi \sqrt{\pm g_{ij} u^i u^j}, \quad (\pm g_{ij} A_k u^i u^j u^k)^{1/3}. \tag{15}$$

The interaction with the tensor field warrants a close inspection. The Euler equation is

$$\frac{d}{d\chi} \left[\frac{g_{ij} u^j}{\sqrt{\pm g_{kl} u^k u^l}} \right] - \tfrac{1}{2} \frac{g_{jk,i} u^k u^j}{\sqrt{\pm g_{lm} u^l u^m}} = 0. \tag{16}$$

The first term in this equation we shall call the "inertial force" and the second a "gravitational force." Because of the arbitrary choice of coordinate system the division between the two forces is coordinate-dependent. The bracketed expression in the first term might be called the "momentum" P_i of the particle. This definition is independent of the choice of χ. The significance of the "momentum" becomes more clear by choosing coordinates which reduce g_{ij} locally to the form

$$\eta_{ij} = \begin{bmatrix} 1 & & & \\ & 1 & & \\ & & 1 & \\ & & & \pm 1 \end{bmatrix} \tag{17}$$

The first three diagonal elements must have the same sign, because of isotropy, arbitrarily chosen as $(+)$. The fourth element, associated with "time", may have either sign depending upon the signature of g_{ij}. Choosing χ to be coordinate time x^4, the bracket becomes

$$P_4 = \frac{\pm 1}{\sqrt{1 \pm v^2}} \qquad u^4 = 1$$

$$u^\alpha = v^\alpha = \frac{dx^\alpha}{dx^4} \tag{18}$$

$$P_\alpha = \frac{v^\alpha}{\sqrt{1 \pm v^2}} \qquad v^2 = \sum_1^3 (v^\alpha)^2$$

These equations can now be discussed. Consistent with Mach's principle, we wish to consider inertial forces as having their origin in a field: a long-range field having its origin in the distant matter of the universe. Acceleration-dependent forces do not appear in an Euler equation until the Lagrangian contains u^i quadratically. Because of the arbitrary choice of χ, this requires an interaction with at least a 2nd rank tensor. Thus to get agreement with observations requires at least one long-range tensor field most simply taken as 2nd rank.

The question of signature can now be settled. To get a connection between momentum and velocity in the usual form requires the minus sign in (18). One should accept this with a bit of caution, however. It should be remembered that this particular coordinate system and v^α are not necessarily the coordinates and velocity appropriate to laboratory physics. However, to anticipate a bit, if gravitation is described by only one tensor of this type, or by a tensor and a scalar field, it can be demonstrated that the v^α is that measured in the laboratory. If there were two tensor interactions there would be no requirement that they should both have a negative signature.

It is obvious that we have enumerated the ingredients of a possible action principle of colossal magnitude. Instead of writing this essentially meaningless equation we will construct a few examples.

The requirement that we have inertial forces and electromagnetism requires the presence of a long-range tensor and vector field. The simplest action principle which we can construct describing:

(1) The self-interaction of the tensor field
(2) The interaction between the vector and tensor field
(3) The interaction between the tensor field and the particles
(4) The interaction between the vector field and the particles
is the following:

$$0 = \delta \int [R + g^{ij}g^{kl}F_{ik}F_{jl} + \sum \int (m\sqrt{-g_{ij}u^iu^j} + eA_iu^i)\frac{\delta^4(x - \bar{x})}{\sqrt{-g}}d\chi]\sqrt{-g}\,d^4x \tag{19}$$

The sum is to be taken over the various particles which will generally differ in the constants m and e, and which will have coordinates $\bar{x}^i(\chi)$, $u^i = d\bar{x}^i/d\chi$. It should be noted with satisfaction that the form of the term coupling the particle to A_i, a form demanded by the arbitrariness in χ, is consistent with the requirement that the coupling be linear in A_i, a strong condition imposed by the lack of a self-interaction in the photon field.

It should be noted that the quadratic term $g^{ij}A_iA_j$ is missing from equation (19). This is because of the precision charge equality experiments[20] which strongly suggest a guage invariant vector theory of electromagnetism. The term $\lambda \sqrt{-g}$, with λ a constant, is omitted because this gives the graviton a mass and shortens its range.

If the Euler equations derived from equation (19) have been solved, at least in principle, it is safe to consider geometrical problems. In this connection it is convenient to choose χ in such a way as to make

$$-g_{ij}u^iu^j = 1. \tag{20}$$

The resulting χ will be designated by τ and called "proper time." This is a reasonable definition as it is easily seen that this is the time that would be measured by an atomic clock moving with the particle. In order to see this, choose a coordinate system to be locally Minkowskian (equation (17) with first derivatives of $g_{ij} = \eta_{ij}$ zero). Also choose the coordinate system so that the particle (atom) is at rest. The equations of motion for the atomic particles, considered to be in this known and given field and neglecting gravitational interactions between them, are given by the variational principle, equation (19) with R dropped and $g_{ij} = \eta_{ij}$. This is a unique equation and leads to unique equations of motion. The characteristic period of the atom would be some unique coordinate time interval Δx^4 (with $\Delta x^\alpha = 0$ for $\alpha = 1, 2, 3$) independent of the location of the atom. The uniqueness follows from uniqueness of the equations of motion.

From equation (20) we obtain

$$d\tau^2 = - g_{ij} \, dx^i \, dx^j \tag{21}$$

and we find for the coordinate intervals representing one clock period the result

$$\Delta\tau^2 = - \eta_{ij}\Delta x^i \Delta x^j = (\Delta x^4)^2 \tag{22}$$

$$\Delta\tau = \Delta x^4.$$

Hence, for this choice of coordinate system, $\Delta\tau$ measures the period of a clock which changes coordinates by an amount Δx^1 during one period. But $\Delta\tau$ is an invariant and measures this period for any coordinate system. In similar fashion $\Delta\tau$ can give an invariant measure of the diameter of an atom and hence provide a unit of length.

From equation (18), with the choice of the minus sign, $v = 1$ is the upper limit for the velocity of any particle. A particle has a finite momentum in the limit as $v \to 1$ only if its mass tends to zero. Hence, massless particles all move with the same characteristic velocity (in particular, photons).

From equation (21), in locally Minkowski coordinates.

$$\left(\frac{d\tau}{dx^4}\right)^2 = 1 - v^2. \tag{23}$$

If dx^i represents an infinitesimal coordinate interval connection by a light ray (photon), $v = 1$ and $d\tau = 0$.

The variational equation (equation (19)) for a particle interacting only with the tensor field is

$$0 = \delta \int m \sqrt{- g_{ij}u^i u^j} \, d\tau \tag{24}$$

$$0 = \delta \int d\tau$$

Hence, the particle moves in such a way as to give a stationary value to τ along its path.

These elementary results have been spelled out in tedious fashion only to make quite clear how the tensor field determines the geometry, if the geometry is measured by atomic rods and clocks or by the geodesic motion of particles: Either definition can be used. If an atom is defined as having a constant diameter and period, the geometry it measures is Riemannian with g_{ij} as the metric tensor. Alternatively, the same geometry is measured if chargeless particles are defined as moving on geodesic paths and light rays are said to move on null geodesics.

The reader should be forewarned that this direct relation between the tensor field and the geometry measured by real rods and clocks, or by particle paths assumed geodesic, disappears if there are other long-range fields.

Let us consider now another possible set of interactions. The following action principle[21] has appeared in the literature.

$$0 = \delta \int [\varphi^2 R - 4\omega g^{ij}\varphi_{,i}\varphi_{,j} + g^{ij}g^{kl}F_{ik}F_{jl} + \sum \int (m\sqrt{- g_{ij}u^i u^j} +$$

$$+ e A_i u^i) \frac{\delta^4(x - \bar{x})}{\sqrt{- g}} \, d\chi] \sqrt{- g} \, d^4x. \tag{25}$$

(Actually it is not quite the same. The φ in equation (25) is the square of that in Reference 21. ω is a constant.) Equation (25) is the same as equation (19) modified by adding a term and by modifying the R term in (19) to represent the interaction of a scalar field with the tensor field only. As equation (25) is quadratic and homogeneous in φ, it represents a linear scalar field without direct sources. As the scalar field does not interact with the particles, they continue to measure a geometry based on g_{ij} interpreted as the metric tensor.

Another possible way of including an interaction of a scalar field is with the variational principle

$$0 = \delta \int [R + \varphi_{,i}\varphi_{,j}g^{ij} + \varphi g^{ij}g^{kl}F_{ik}F_{jl} + \sum \int (m \sqrt{- g_{ij}u^i u^j} +$$

$$+ e A_i u^i) \frac{\delta^4(x - \bar{x})}{\sqrt{- g}} \, d\chi] \sqrt{- g} \, d^4x. \tag{26}$$

It represents, in addition to the other features of equation (19), a scalar field interacting with the tensor and vector fields. The Euler equation for φ is inhomogeneous in φ, with the electromagnetic Lagrangian density serving as the source of φ. The

Euler equation for A_i is interesting as it describes an electromagnetic field in a medium with variable dielectric constant ϵ and permeability μ

$$\epsilon = \mu^{-1} = \varphi. \tag{27}$$

This results in the fine structure constant being variable, varying as

$$\alpha = \frac{e^2}{\varphi \hbar c}. \tag{28}$$

The e in equations (26) and (28) is the "true charge" and is constant.

As discussed in the text, possible variations of α are extremely small, making a variational principle of the form of equation (26) unlikely.

In similar fashion an action principle can be constructed which makes the coupling constant to the pion field, or any other field, a function of a scalar. Only the gauge invariant vector field, because of its property of a strongly conserved source, requires the scalar coupling to the term $g^{ij}g^{kl}F_{ik}F_{jl}$. For these other fields, the coupling constant of the field may contain the φ linearity. In equation (26), e cannot be replaced by φ as the resulting Euler equation for A_i requires that φ be constant.

Another possible action principle is obtained by taking as the source of the φ field the classical particles. The action principle in this case is:

$$0 = \delta \int [R + g^{ij}\varphi_{,i}\varphi_{,j} + g^{ij}g^{kl}F_{ik}F_{jl} + \sum \int (m\varphi \sqrt{-g_{ij}u^iu^j} +$$

$$+ e A_i u^i) \frac{\delta^4(x - \bar{x})}{\sqrt{-g}} d\chi] \sqrt{-g} \, d^4x. \tag{29}$$

With the assumption that all particle masses contain the term φ, the effect of the scalar field disappears in laboratory physics as long as gravitational interactions between the particles in the laboratory are neglected (i.e., both the scalar and tensor interactions). (These fields are to be treated as known and given.) This is seen by dropping the first two terms in equation (29), and by substituting for g_{ij} the relation

$$g_{ij} = \varphi^{-2}\bar{g}_{ij}.$$

If this is done, equation (29) becomes

$$0 = \delta \int (\bar{g}^{ij}\bar{g}^{kl}F_{ik}F_{jl} + \sum \int (m \sqrt{-\bar{g}_{ij}u^iu^j} +$$

$$+ e A_i u^i) \frac{\delta^4(x - \bar{x})}{\sqrt{-\bar{g}}} d\chi] \sqrt{-\bar{g}} \, d^4x. \tag{30}$$

and the scalar field does not appear explicitly. It must be emphasized that this would also be true if other fields, such as the pion field, were included, providing their masses contained the scalar factor φ.

The previously used argument (equations (20)–(24)) could again be invoked to show that ordinary rods and clocks would measure a geometry with $\bar{g}_{ij}$ as the metric tensor, not g_{ij}.

These remarks should not be taken to imply that the scalar is unobservable, for the dimensionless gravitational coupling constant $Gm^2{}_p/\hbar c$, with m_p the mass of any elementary particle, becomes

$$\frac{\varphi^2 m^2{}_p}{16\pi\hbar c} \tag{31}$$

when equation (29) is taken as the action principle. The $\hbar$ does not appear explicitly in this equation, but it would have if the pion field had been included as a classical Boson field.

It is evident that we could construct numerous other action principles. We could introduce two or more zero mass tensor fields or two vector fields, the first representing gravitation and the second a vector contribution to the gravitational field[22,23]. It becomes the problem for the experimentalist to narrow down this enormous range of theories and pick out that subclass compatible with the observations.

It must be emphasized that the assumption of the equivalence principle (strong form) eliminates all theories but one, for the requirement that there be no space anisotropy eliminates all but one tensor field, the requirement that gravitational accelerations be equal eliminates a vector contribution to gravitation, and the requirement of identical numerical content in the laws of physics everywhere (when expressed in locally inertial coordinates (eliminates a scalar field. Many will feel a strong compulsion to accept *a priori* the strong equivalence principle. The author does not, but, as an experimentalist, would much prefer to consider a larger class of theories and to narrow it down experimentally. If this is done, the extremely stringent requirements of the Hughes–Drever experiment and the Eötvös experiment appear to narrow down the class to some combination of a single tensor field and a scalar field interacting only with the tensor field, or else with the tensor field and all particles through their mass terms.

Finally, it must again be emphasized that the introduction of a metrical geometry always requires an arbitrary assumption. Only when the gravitational effects are all due to a single tensor field (Einstein's theory) can this assumption be made to appear unique, the one choice of metric tensor being much prettier than all others.

Appendix 5

Cosmology, Mach's Principle and Relativity

R. H. Dicke

Reprinted from the *I.C.S.U. Review*. Vol. 5 (1963) pp. 40–53

Cosmology is one of the most enchanting of the sciences, for man cannot contemplate the tremendous stretch of the universe, its origins and evolution, without feeling a bit humble. Having its roots in philosophic speculation, cosmology evolved gradually into a physical science, but a science with so little observational basis that philosophical considerations still play a crucial if not dominant role. From observations made on galaxies in the unobscured 70 per cent of the sky, made mostly in the northern hemisphere, observations which show a decided tendency for galaxies to cluster, it is concluded, in spite of the clustering, that the universe is basically isotropic after ignoring "small" scale inhomogenieties. Although these observations were made on a limited volume of space only, and from a single vantage point, we surmise that we would see this same idealized isotropic distribution from any point of observation.

Other observations are even more uncertain. Our knowledge of the density of matter in space is obtained from the visible matter, the stars in galaxies. Virtually nothing is known about intergalactic matter. The observationally determined Hubble expansion age of the universe is believed to be fairly reliable, but the fact that it has doubled twice in a decade shakes ones confidence in this number. While the new radio observations are beginning to provide badly needed supplementary information, the primary need of cosmology continues to be more observations.

Despite the deficiencies in the observational basis of cosmology, it has been possible to lift it above the level of conjecture. This is due largely to the use of a powerful theoretical tool, that of relativistic mechanics.

Perhaps the most important thing to be said about the principles of relativity in relation to the cosmological problem is that these principles provide a rigid framework, a formal structure that delimits and helps to define the conclusions to be derived from the observations. In a very real sense the host of laboratory experiments performed by physicists, mostly with high energy particle accelerators, experiments that help to establish the validity of the relativistic principles, are cosmological observations, for the general principles thereby established are directly applicable to the cosmological problem.

While relativity is a strong tool provided by physicists for dealing with the cosmological problem, its early origins are actually to be found in cosmology. In the early eighteenth century Bishop G. Berkeley,[1] the British philosopher, in commenting upon Newton's concept of an absolute physical space remarked that this concept was without a physical basis, for a vacuum, devoid of all physical objects, was divested of physical properties, points, lines, and positional relations being meaningless for such an empty *physical* space. Thus Newton's idea of the motion of a body with respect to such an absolute space was a concept devoid of physical significance. Around 1710 Bishop Berkeley wrote,[2] "Let us imagine two globes and that besides them nothing material exists, then the motion in a circle of these two globes round their common centre cannot be imagined. But suppose that the heaven of fixed stars suddenly created and we shall be in a position to imagine the motion of the globes by their relative position to different parts of the heavens".

Bishop Berkeley's insistence that the only meaningful motion of a body was motion *relative* to other matter is the *relativity principle*. This idea recurs in the writings of Mach[3] and in the theory of relativity as it was developed by Einstein[4] and others.

Mach asserted that, assuming the validity of the relativity principle, the inertial forces appearing in an accelerated laboratory must have their origin in the distant matter of the universe, for the accelerated motion could with equal right be considered to be that of distant matter relative to the laboratory. Note the cosmological significance of this idea, and the dominant role assigned by Mach to the distant matter of the universe. According to him, this influence of distant matter penetrates the electrically shielded walls of the laboratory, affecting the physicist's every experiment. This is an idea of grand proportions, for if it is right the universe is much more than the sum of independent parts. The laboratory is tied to and influenced by matter in the remote parts of the universe. If Mach's interpretation of inertia is correct, it might be expected that inertial effects would depend upon the distribution of matter about the point in question. The physicist could ill afford to ignore cosmology under these conditions.

Physical Space

The concepts of an absolute physical space and an absolute time are deeply entrenched. Thus it is difficult to conceive of a physical space, not necessarily Euclidean, a space devoid of points and lines determined *a priori*, a space in which the geometrical properties are physical in origin, being derived from the matter contained in the space.

Consider a situation in which space is flooded with particles of various kinds, interacting with each other, some perhaps being created and annihilated during these interactions. It is clear that, ideally at least, physical events such as the collision between two particles could be used to define in a meaningful (i.e. invariant) way a point in a 4-dimensional space-time. An electron interacting with a host of photons could define a geometrical point at each such interaction. The sequence of points (events) could define the space-time trajectory of the electron. Each such point could be labeled with a 4-fold set of numbers (coordinates) almost arbitrarily chosen.

If photons were present in a region of space in large numbers, their effects, on the average, might be described by an electromagnetic field, the two Maxwell invariants of which could be used, in principle at least, to help locate a point anywhere in the space occupied by the photons. For example, if E and B represent electric and magnetic field components, the Maxwell invariants $E \cdot B$ and $B^2 - E^2$ could be measured at a given point and their values used as two out of 4 parameters required to physically label the point. Other fields could provide more invariants or alternate invariants.[5] This scheme obviously fails if the various fields are null fields for which the invariants are all zero.

It should be noted that in this illustrative example it was the Maxwell *invariants*, not field components, which were used to help characterize the points in space physically. These numbers are independent of the orientation and motion of the observer who makes the measurements. Thus they are free of conditions imposed *a priori* by a geometrical coordinate system. This is essential if the concept of a geometrical point is to be divorced from the characterization of an absolute space.

The key idea to be wrung from the relativity principle is the following: Observables, results of measurements by a specific apparatus on a specific physical system are invariants, independent of coordinate system, being dependent only upon the relation of the measuring apparatus to the physical system. The appropriate mathematical formulation of the kinematic and dynamical relations of physics is provided by tensor analysis, for the language of tensors is a language based on coordinates in general, not specific coordinate systems. This has proved to be the key idea; physical events take place in a 4-dimensional space-time continuum and the laws of physics are to be stated in invariant form using the language of tensor analysis. This key idea unlocks the big door that leads to the relativity theory.

Fields

By requiring that fields, such as gravitation or electromagnetism, be represented by tensors, the range of possible fields is very much limited, and these possibilities are well classified. Thus fields (classical) may be classified as scalar, vector, tensor and higher rank tensor. We shall assume, perhaps without good reason, that higher rank tensor fields do not exist.

The scalar field is given by a single invariant function of coordinates $\varphi(\eta)$. If the coordinate system is changed, φ is defined as unchanged at the new coordinates corresponding to the old point in space. A contravariant vector B^i is a set of four functions which transform under coordinate transformations like the coordinate differentials dx^i, namely

$$dx^i = \frac{\partial x_i}{\partial \bar{x}^j} \, d\bar{x}^j$$

and

$$B^i = \frac{\partial x_i}{\partial \bar{x}^j} \, \bar{B}^j$$

(Note that $i = 1, 2, 3, 4$ is not a power of B but an index label. The sum over the repeated index $j = 1, \text{ - - - } 4$ is to be understood.) In similar fashion the covariant vector B^i transforms like the prototype of all such vectors $\theta_{,i} = d\eta^i/\partial x^i$, where θ is a scalar, namely

$$B_i = \frac{\partial \bar{x}^j}{\partial x^i} \, \bar{B}_j$$

It should be noted that the inner product $A_i \, B^i$ is a scalar. The extension to tensor fields is straightforward. The tensor g_{ij} transforms like

$$g_{ij} = \bar{g}_{kl} \frac{\partial \bar{x}^k}{\partial x^i} \frac{\partial \bar{x}^l}{\partial x^j} \tag{1}$$

If the path of a particle is parametrized by an arbitrary chosen monotonically increasing variable χ (invariant), the velocity' $U^i = d\eta^i/d\chi$ is a contravariant vector, where x^i refers to coordinates in an arbitrarily coordinate system. If there exists a covariant vector field A_i, the product $A_i U^i$ is an invariant.

It should be remarked parenthetically at this stage that the only geometrical concepts so far employed are those of the 4-dimensional space-time continuum and the labeling with smoothly varying but otherwise arbitrarily chosen coordinates of events in this 4-dimensional manifold. Nothing has been said about metric, geodesic curves, or curvature, for these concepts are meaningful only after units of length and time are defined. In a very real sense, the "metry" in geometry is to be taken seriously. The geometry of a physical space is not a property of the space alone. It also involves the means of "measuring" the space. As meter sticks and clocks are physical objects, they will be affected by physical fields and the "geometry" based on such objects will be affected by these fields. In order to avoid the concept of an absolute space and a geometry introduced *a priori*, the question of the space-time measure, and spatial metric, should be ignored at this stage.

As there is a possible arbitrariness in the units and methods of measure, the dynamical behavior of a physical system must be independent of the choice made. Hence it is both possible and desirable to discuss the dynamical behavior of a physical system without specifying closely the geometry of space.

If it be assumed that the motion of a particle interacting only with a vector field is derivable from a variational principle, the variational equation is uniquely defined, for the integrand $A_i U^i$ is the only invariant which can be constructed from A_i and U^i such that the integral over χ, namely

$$\int A_i U^i \, d\chi \tag{2}$$

is independent of the choice of the arbitrary invariant parameter χ. By requiring that this integral between fixed limits take on a value which is an extremum one finds that the motion of the particle is such that

$$0 = \frac{dA_i}{d\chi} - A_{j,i} U^j = (A_{i,j} - A_{j,i}) U^j \tag{3}$$

At this point one cannot fail to be struck by the power of the relativity principle, for a close examination of equation (3) shows that the right side of this equation has the same form as, and might be taken to represent, a measure of the electromagnetic force acting on a charged particle.

Thus, if this vector field be interpreted as electromagnetism, equation (3) states that the particle moves in such a way as to make the electro-magnetic force (Lorentz) acting on the particle zero. Charged particles do not actually move this way, but this is another story to which we shall return shortly. Here we should simply note that the complex electromagnetic forces fall in a natural way out of the basic assumptions of invariance plus the assumption that electromagnetism is described by a covariant vector field. The covariant vector A_i has four components, essentially the three components of the "vector potential" of classical electromagnetism and the "scalar potential", a total of 4. These names refer to 3-space transformation properties, not to be confused with the more general 4-space general coordinate transformations.

Cosmic Fields

The electromagnetic field describes the properties of large numbers of photons in bulk. These particles have zero mass, travelling always with the same speed (of light). The only field capable of a long range quasi-static interaction is that associated with such a zero-mass particle. Thus the slowly changing mass distribution in distant parts of the universe could make its presence felt in the laboratory only through zero mass fields and from the above these fields may be of at least three basic types, scalar, vector and tensor. (Spinor fields are ignored for reasons which cannot be discussed here.)

Assuming the validity of relativistic principles, these fields, which can be conveniently called cosmic fields, are of the type which in the past, and to this day, determine the gross features of the evolution of the universe, for these are the only types of quasistatic interactions which can extend over great distances. For simplicity we shall assume that there is at most one field of each type. (The evidence for this is fairly good but cannot be discussed here.)

If it be assumed that Maxwell's electromagnetic equations are valid and that the universe over large volume averages is isotropic, the vector field electro magnetism cannot play a role on the large cosmological scale. The reason for this is the assumed isotropy of the matter distribution which would require both the electric and magnetic fields to vanish over large volume averages and, consequently, the vanishing of electric charge and current (over large volume averages).

Several years ago Lyttleton and Bondi[6] proposed modified electromagnetic equations, non gauge-invariant, such that charge was not strictly conserved. With this assumption cosmological influences of distant matter through the vector field was possible. However, the extremely precise charge equality measurement of King[7] can be used to exclude the Lyttleton–Bondi hypothesis.

Apparently we should limit ourselves to scalar and tensor fields in looking for cosmic interactions. Returning for the moment to equation (3) it is evident that the element that is missing in order to obtain a sensible equation of motion is an inertial force, for as formulated by Lorentz, a charged particle moves in such a way as to make the sum of the Lorentz force and the inertial reaction zero.

It is evident from equation (3) that the vector force is velocity dependent. It is evident that this force is independent of the acceleration of the particle because the variational equation (2) contains the four-velocity linearity only. If the variational equation contains the velocity quadratically, the Euler equation contains a term with a derivative of the velocity. To form an invariant quadratic in velocity a tensor is needed. Apparently inertial forces can occur only after a tensor field is introduced. We shall assume that there exists a long range tensor field (associated with chargeless zero-mass particles with a spin angular momentum of $2\hbar$).

This tensor field, generated by matter in distant parts of the universe, must supply the local inertial effects discussed by Berkeley and Mach. The precession of a gyroscope, relative to the rotating earth and continuing to point always in some fixed direction relative to distant matter of the universe, may be considered the result of its interacting with a tensor field having its origin primarily in this enormous amount of matter ($\sim 10^{56}\,g$) at a great distance (up to $\sim 10^{10}$ light years).

In order to modify equation (2) to include the interaction with a tensor field, we replace it by the variational equations

$$0 = \delta \int [m(g_{ij} U^i U^j)^{1/2} + e A_i U^i] d\chi \qquad (4)$$

where e and m are constants introduced to characterize the "charge" and "mass" of the particle. Equation (4) is the only one which can be written depending upon a linear combination of the two interactions, and such that the parameter χ may be chosen arbitrarily. The Euler equation obtained from equation (4) (equivalent to equation (3)) is

$$0 = \frac{d}{d\chi}\left(\frac{m g_{ij} U^j}{\sqrt{g_{kl} U^k U^l}}\right) - \tfrac{1}{2}\frac{m g_{kl,i}\, U^k U^l}{(g_{kl} U^k U^l)^{1/2}} - e F_{ij} U^j \qquad (5)$$

with

$$F_{ij} = A_{i,j} - A_{j,i} = \frac{\partial A_i}{\partial x^j} - \frac{\partial A_j}{\partial x^i} \tag{6}$$

It is apparent that the first term of equation (5) contains an acceleration dependent force. In a sense the whole term represents the inertial force since it is in the form of a rate of change with respect to "time" of the "momentum" of the particle. The last term is the electromagnetic force already discussed, which has its origin in locally produced electric fields rather than in distant parts of the universe. The second term is a bonus. It represents a force quadratic in velocity and is found upon closer examination to represent the gravitational force. In a sense, both of the first two terms represent gravitational force which acts upon the body when it is accelerated.

The second term represents a gravitational force present only if there are non-zero gradients in one or more tensor components. The dichotomy between inertial and gravitational forces is artificial, being coordinate dependent. It can be shown that there always are coordinate systems such that

$$g_{jk,i} = \frac{\partial g_{jk}}{\partial x^i} = 0 \tag{7}$$

for any one point in the space. For this choice of coordinate system the gravitational force is zero at this point.

The condition given by equation (7) allows considerable arbitrariness in the coordinate transformation and it is possible in addition to impose the condition that at the point in question, after the coordinate transformation,

$$
\begin{aligned}
g_{ij} &= 0 & &\text{for } i \neq j \\
g_{\alpha\alpha} &= \pm 1 & &\text{for } \alpha = 1, 2, 3 \\
g_{44} &= 1
\end{aligned}
\tag{8}
$$

The first three diagonal terms are associated with space-like intervals and because of spatial isotropy have the same sign, not yet specified. The $4th$ is to be interpreted as associated with time.

There are numerous reasons, mainly obtained from experiments with high energy particles, for believing that there is an upper limit to the velocity of a particle. As the velocity approaches this upper limit its momentum must approach infinity. It can be seen from equation (5), after substituting equations (7) and (8), that the proper choice of sign in equation (8) is minus and with this choice

$$\frac{m U^j}{(g_{kl} U^k U^l)^{1/2}} \to \infty \text{ as } \sum_{\alpha+1, 2, 3} \left(\frac{dx^\alpha}{dx^4} \right)^2 \to 1 \tag{9}$$

Clearly, for this choice of coordinate system $v^2 = 1$ is the upper limit for the square of the speed of a particle. This upper limit can be reached with a finite momentum (see equation 5) only for a massless particle ($m = 0$), hence massless particles such as photons and gravitons (associated with the tensor field g_{ij}) must travel with the same characteristic velocity, that of light.

If the above substitutions are made in equation (5) and the parameter χ is replaced by x^4, one obtains for the four equations after writing the Lorentz force in conventional form and introducing vector notation

$$-\frac{d}{dt}\left(\frac{mv}{\sqrt{1-v^2}}\right) = -e(E + v \times B) \tag{10}$$

where $i = 1, 2, 3$ and

$$\frac{d}{dt}\left(\frac{m}{\sqrt{1-v^2}}\right) = ev{\cdot}E \tag{10a}$$

where $i = 4$, with $dt = dx^4$. The $4th$ equation is recognized as stating that the work done on the particle by electromagnetic forces is equal to the change in its energy. It is clear from equations (5)–(10) how the tensor field g_{ij} is the source of the prosaic inertial force (the left side of equation 10a).

It is clear from the above that the long range tensor field, through the acceleration dependent force which it generates, is a cosmic force par excellence. For its influence, propagated from distant parts of the universe, permeates insidiously the thickest and best shielded walls of the physicists inner sanctum, affecting all his measurements.

But one cosmic field remains for discussion, the scalar field φ. For reasons which to this writer are inadequate it is usually considered to be non-existent. If it be assumed tentatively to exist, and to act on a particle, the variational equation (4) must be modified to include its effect. A close examination of the effect of a scalar interaction shows that it destroys the constancy of m, making m a function of φ. The only change to be made in equation (4) therefore is to assume that m is a function of φ. The same functional dependence must be assumed for all matter, or the composition independence of the gravitational acceleration is destroyed.

For laboratory physics the observable effects of a scalar field, externally provided, are almost non-existent. If the mass m is of the form $m = m_0 f(\varphi)$ with m_0 constant, the function f may be absorbed under the square root in equation (4) and combined with g_{ij} to give a new effective g_{ij}, $g_{ij} = f^2 g_{ij}$. However, there is always a choice of coordinate system for which locally equations (7) and (8) are satisfied with g_{ij} in place of g_{ij}. Then equations of the form of equation (10) are satisfied with m replaced by m_0. The only place that the scalar φ would creep into laboratory experiments would be in connection with gravitational measurements, for the gravitational coupling constant

$$\frac{Gm^2}{\hbar e} = \frac{Gm_0^2}{\hbar e}f^2 \tag{11}$$

depends explicitly upon f. (In equation (11) m refers to the mass of some elementary particle such as a proton.) It is conceivable that the weak coupling constant associated with β decay is also explicitly dependent on particle mass, hence on f.

Cosmic Fields and Geometry

It is to be recalled that geometrical concepts, beyond a simple coordinate labeling of space-time points, have not yet been interjected. The introduction of a metric into the geometry can be carried out as soon as definitions of units of length and time are given. The concept of measure is dependent upon means and units of measure.

If for the moment the scalar field is assumed to be non-existent, the choice of units is natural and almost unambiguous. Characteristic atomic radii and periods (meter sticks and clocks built from atoms) may be chosen to represent units of measure. With this choice of geometrical measure it is found that the tensor g_{ij} represents the metric tensor of the geometry. This may be readily seen by noting that for the special point in the special coordinate system, given by the conditions of equations (7) and (8), the classical equations of motion of electrons take on a uniquely specified standard form (10). (The same would be true of the quantum mechanical equation.) Thus in terms of a measure based on these coordinates the atom assumes some definite fixed size and period. But from equation (8) (sign minus) the invariant

$$ds^2 = g_{ij}\, dx^i dx^j$$

represents a measure of the diameter or period of the atom for this case. That is to say, if a diameter of an atom is given by $dx^1 = D$, $dx^2 = dx^3 = dx^4 = 0$, one has $ds^2 = -D^2$, hence ds^2 measures the diameter. As ds is an invariant, it represents a measure of length (or time) for all coordinate systems. Thus g_{ij} represents the metric tensor of a Riemannian geometry.

When a scalar field is present, the choice of units of length and time is not nearly so unambiguous. If measurements are made in such a way as to treat the mass of an elementary particle, Planck's constant, and the velocity of light as constant by definition, the gravitational constant becomes $G f^2$ and is variable. Under these conditions, a geometrical measure of space carried out with the atom providing units of length and time would find that the tensor $\bar{g}_{ij}$ can be interpreted as the metric tensor of a Riemannian geometry. If, however, units of measure are provided by defining G, $\hbar$, and c as constant, the tensor $\bar{g}_{ij}$ plays the role of the metric tensor.[11] The first gravitational theory combining the effects of a tensor and scalar field was formulated by Jordan.[8] This was a theory which attempted to give a formal basis to the cosmological idea of Dirac.[9] Later the same type of formalism was used by Brans and Dicke in connection with a discussion of Mach's principle.[10] The equivalence of the Brans–Dicke formalism with a "general relativity" theory was later shown by using a units transformation.[11]

The scalar field, if it exists, carries into the laboratory a cosmological effect, additional to the easily observed inertial effect. Within the framework of a cosmology with a scalar field, it was found that the gravitational coupling constant Gm^2/hc would be expected to have a value of the order of magnitude the age of the universe (expressed in atomic time units) divided by the mass of the visible part (expressed in particle mass units).[10] Expressed in physical terms, it has the extremely small value of $1.8 \cdot 10^{-38}$ (expressed in terms of the proton mass) because of the large value of the scalar, generated by the enormous amounts of matter in the universe. This value $\sim 10^{-38}$ agrees roughly with the values calculated from the above relation using the observed mass density of the universe. It would be expected to vary as the universe expands. Dirac[9] was the first to suggest a connection between the mass content of the universe, its size, and the gravitational coupling "constant".

Of particular significance is the fact that the gravitational "constant" would be expected to decrease with time. Assuming an evolving universe, the scalar field would change with time because of the general expansion of the universe. This would decrease the strength of the gravitational interaction.

To return briefly to the relativity theme of the first part of this paper, Einstein's "general relativity", a rather special relativity theory for which the scalar field is assumed not to exist, appears to be more nearly a theory of an absolute space than that of a relativistic space. This has been emphasized by Synge in his new book.[12] There are several reasons for this: First, Einstein's field equation for g_{ij} has solutions for empty space in the form of flat space metrics. From the point of view of Mach such solutions are meaningless. Second, the space about a localized mass distribution becomes asymptotically flat at infinity and there is, in principle, nothing to keep one from journeying arbitrarily far into this twighlight zone where inertial effects should disappear. Third, the gravitational acceleration of the earth toward the sun, according to Einstein, is independent of the amount of distant matter isotropically distributed about the sun. According to Mach's ideas concerning the origin of inertia, this acceleration should be dependent upon the total mass distribution. In the opinion of this author, Synge is correct, Einstein's theory (in its usual form) is actually not a relativity theory; it is more nearly the theory of an absolute 4-dimensional geometry. It is beyond the scope of this article to discuss these matters in detail, in particular to consider the significance of boundary conditions and space closure with respect to Mach's principle. (See discussions by J. A. Wheeler, also by Hönl, on this problem.)

The addition of a scalar field, with a suitable boundary condition on the scalar, changes the situation.[10] (1) There is no solution at all for an empty space; (2) Space closes about a localized mass configuration making it impossible to journey into the never-never land of inertialess space; (3) The acceleration of the earth toward the sun depends upon the value of the scalar at the solar system, in turn depending upon the amount of matter at great distance.

Cosmic Fields and Cosmology

We have seen that the physicist can ill afford to ignore cosmology, for insidious cosmological effects penetrate the walls of his laboratory, affecting all his experiments. The two long range cosmic fields, certainly tensor and possibly scalar, determine also the gross evolutionary history of the universe. The third long range field, electromagnetism, probably plays an important role on a smaller scale only, with distances of the order of a galactic diameter being the characteristic size of electromagnetic elements.

In turning to more specific cosmological questions, we first write the Einstein field equation for the tensor g_{ij} (assuming no scalar field exists).

$$R_{ij} - \tfrac{1}{2}g_{ij}\,R + \Lambda\,g_{ij} = -\frac{8\pi G}{c^4}\,T_{ij} \tag{12}$$

Here R_{ij} is a curvature tensor, a tensor measure of the curvature of space with g_{ij} interpreted as the metric tensor of the space. In similar fashion R is a scalar measure of curvature. T_{ij} is the energy-momentum tensor of matter.

The third term on the left is a bone of contention among relativists and cosmologists. The term A is the reciprocal of the square of a characteristic length, a length which must be huge $\sim 10^{28}$ cm. The cosmological term was first introduced by Einstein, *ad hoc*, in an attempt to obtain equations describing a static universe. When it became apparent from Hubble's observations that the universe was actually expanding, he dropped the term. Because of the enormous characteristic length which this term introduces, and the inelegant variational principle from which equation (12) is derived, most specialists in general relativity also drop this term. On the other hand some cosmologists, pointing to the discrepancies in age patterns[13] with stars apparently older than the Hubble expansion age of the universe, retain this term to help obtain consistency. The author is inclined to drop the cosmological term until its existence is clearly forced by observations. It is evident, however, that decisions such as this are based more on formal considerations and philosophy than upon observations. V will be assumed to be zero in the remainder of this article.

The next important problem which a cosmologist must face involves the question of isotropy. If the universe is everywhere isotropic, it is uniform and the field equations[12] are enormously simplified by this uniformity. Without this simplifying assumption the equations are too general and the observations too few to limit the class of possible solutions to a reasonable number. But still it is difficult to support the assumption with observations. Thus Heckmann has pointed out that a certain type of departure from isotropy could have had drastic effects early in the expansion of the universe and now be essentially unobservable.

Here again a decision must be based primarily on matters of philosophy. One assumes the simplest situation compatible with the observations, namely a roughly uniform and isotropic universe. Without this assumption it is essentially impossible to choose between the large number of possible alternatives. However, we stretch the fibres of credulity too far if we believe that this assumption is valid all the way back to the start of the expansion of an infinitely dense universe of zero radius. One important question to answer eventually is, "How far back in time, if at all, is this assumption valid?"

If the assumption of isotropy and uniformity is made, several important conclusions can be based on this essentially geometrical fact, conclusions which are based on the kinematics of the universe and are independent of dynamical considerations. There exists a coordinate system, time orthogonal, such that the metric tensor has the form such that the expression for interval is

$$\frac{1}{c^2}\,ds^2 = -\frac{a^2}{(1 + kr^2)^2}\,[(dx^1)^2 + (dx^2)^2 + (dx^3)^2] + dt^2 \tag{13}$$

This describes a system of coordinates such that galaxies, in the mean, occupy fixed space points $x^1 - -x^3$, but that the mesh of this three dimensional coordinate system keeps expanding with time, distances (measured in time units) being proportional to a, a function of time. The time coordinate t is sometimes called cosmic time. It would be measured by a clock on one of these idealized galaxies, stationary in the coordinate mesh. The 3-dimensional subspaces with x^4 constant are of constant curvature (a function of time). As an easily visualizable example of a curved space consider a 2-dimensional surface. A two dimensional surface of constant curvature may be a spherical surface (positive curvature), a plane (zero curvature), or a hyperbolic surface (negative curvature). There are also 3 different types of three dimensional spaces of constant curvature, namely positive, zero, and negative curvature.

While the observational evidence is poor, it is beginning to favor slightly the universe of positive curvature.[14]

If the tensor g_{ij} in the form of equation (13) is substituted into equation (12) equation (14) is obtained,

$$\left(\frac{da}{dt}\right)^2 + k = \frac{8\pi}{3} G\rho a^2 \tag{14}$$

for the expansion parameter a. Here ρ refers to the average matter density of the universe and k takes on the values $+1$, 0, and -1 for closed, flat, and hyperbolic universes.

The Hubble expansion age of the universe (determined from the galactic redshift observations) is given by the expression

$$T_h = a \bigg/ \left(\frac{da}{dt}\right) \tag{15}$$

Another parameter of importance because it can be measured, albeit very imperfectly, is the acceleration parameter.

$$q_0 = -a\frac{d^2a}{dt^2} \bigg/ \left(\frac{da}{dt}\right)^2 = \frac{4\pi}{3} G T_h^2 (\rho + 3P/c^2) \tag{16}$$

where P is the pressure.

Assuming for definiteness (although the observations are not so firm) that the present value of the Hubble age is $T_h = 1.3 \cdot 10^{10}$ years and that of q_0 is ~ 1.0, one finds that the calculated density of matter in the universe is 2.10^{-29} g/cm^3. This calculation is based upon the assumption that the average matter pressure in space is negligible and this result is to be compared with an observed density of visible matter of 10^{-31} g/cm^3.

This vast discrepancy is interpreted by many cosmologists to mean that space contains matter outside the galaxies, perhaps ionized, perhaps neutral but at very low temperature. It has also been suggested that the required energy density may be provided by a vast swarm of the almost unobservable neutrinos. Gravitational waves and scalar waves are another possible source of energy. Such a large amount of energy in the form of massless particles (neutrinos or gravitons) would imply a large pressure in space (2.10^{-8} dynes/cm^2). Some cosmologists interpret the discrepancy as implying that the cosmological term in Einstein's equations, a term which we dropped, must be included.

If pressure in space is negligible, a value of $q_0 > 0.5$ implies that space is closed. If the energy is supplied by neutrinos, gravitons, or scalarons, the conditions for space to close is $q_0 > 1.0$. It is apparent that the observations tend to favor the universe with a closed space. However, the value $q_0 = 1 \pm \frac{1}{2}$ obtained from the observations does not inspire great confidence.[14]

9*

It has been explicitly assumed in the above development that the scalar field is non-existent. If it does exist, surprisingly little modification is needed. Equations (12)–(16) are still valid. However the energy momentum tensor of matter in equation (12) now contains contributions from the scalar field. Also the unit of measure of length is not based on the atom but is taken to be the characteristic length $(Gh/c^3)^{1/2}$. The definition of the metric tensor of the Brans–Dicke theory is based on atomic-standard units of length and time. This (Brans–Dicke) metric tensor is obtained from that for which equation (12) is valid by multiplying by the reciprocal of the field scalar. In similar fashion, to obtain the cosmological expansion parameter of the Brans–Dicke theory, the a of equation (14) is multiplied by $\lambda^{-1/2}$. (The time variable is also multiplied by this factor.) See Reference (11) for the details of this transformation.

For the Brans–Dicke theory, the expansion parameter being based on $\bar{g}_{ij}$, the equation for $\bar{a}$ is a little more complicated. (See reference (10).) However, assuming outgoing wave boundary conditions for the scalar, the solutions of this equation differ surprisingly little from those without the scalar present. An example is plotted in Fig. 1 for the case of a closed space. The parameters have been chosen to correspond with the above assumed values of T_h but with $q_0 = 1.15$. The resulting value for the "age" of the universe is approximately 7.10^9 years. Figure 1 includes a curve for λ, the scalar, which is to be interpreted as proportional to the reciprocal of the gravitational constant.

The curve for $a(t)$ in Fig. 1 is nearly the same shape as that without a scalar field present. Also the gravitational constant given by λ^{-1} in Fig. 1 is not a sufficiently rapidly varying function to make simple a decision between the two theories on the basis of the effect of a greater gravitational interaction, as in the past, on the color and luminosity of distant galaxies.

Steady State Cosmology

Finally it is necessary to make a few remarks about the steady state cosmology of Hoyle,[15] and Bondi and Gold.[16] This is based on the ingenious idea that a continually expanding universe could exist in a steady state, the continuous rarefaction implicit in expansion being vitiated by the creation of new matter. It is visualized that hydrogen materializes in free space, and gathers into galaxies which in turn evolve and disappear through the general expansion process.

Because of the requirements of a steady state, the general expansion process results in the abundance of galaxies decaying exponentially with their age. The mean age of long lived objects, such as galaxies, is $1/3\ T_h \sim 4 \cdot 10^9$ years. The probability of a galaxy being older than $2 \cdot 10^{10}$ years is under 0.01.

One particularly satisfactory aspect of the steady state cosmology is that it provides a constant distribution of distant matter and permits Mach's principle to be satisfied with a constant gravitational coupling "constant".

The ideas encompassed in the steady state cosmology are interesting, but they have not yet been reduced to a satisfactory mathematical formulation complete enough to permit a detailed analysis.

From the standpoint of relativity, the theory appears to be vulnerable to attack on the grounds that it violates fundamental conservation laws, those of energy and momentum. While a quasi-static scalar field, similar to the one introduced by Hoyle,[15] can affect conservation relations by modifying the rest masses of particles, new particles cannot, within the framework of the usual relativistic theories, be created by such a field.

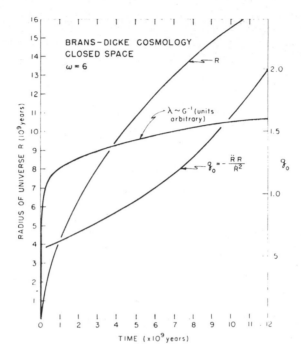

Fig. 1. The expansion parameter $R(=a)$ plotted against time for the Brans–Dicke cosmology. (Also given are the scalar λ and the acceleration parameter q_0).

New particles can be created only by stealing energy and momentum from other particles. If it be presumed that space is filled with high energy particles capable of creating protons, this gas of queer particles would also suffer rarefaction from the expansion.

Notes and References to Appendix 5

[1] G. Berkeley, *The Principles of Human Knowledge* 1710, pp. 111–117, De Motu (1726).

[2] D. Sciama, *The Unity of the Universe* (1959).

[3] E. Mach, *Conservation of Energy*, Open Court Publishing Co., 1872, Note No. 1; *Science of Mechanics*, Open Court Publishing Co., Chicago, Ill., 1883, Chapter II, Section VI.

[4] A. Einstein, *The Meaning of Relativity*, Princeton University Press, p. 99 (1955).

[5] A. Komar, *The Use of Tensor Field Invariants as Invariant Coordinate Labels*, Thesis, Princeton University, 1956 (unpublished).

[6] R. A. Lyttleton and H. Bondi, *Proc. Roy. Soc.*, A **252**, 313 (1959).

[7] J. G. King, *Phys. Rev. Letters*, **5**, 562 (1960).

[8] P. Jordan, *Schwerkraft und Weltall*, Vieweg und Sohn, Braunschweig, 1955; *Z. Physik*, 157, 112, (1959).

[9] P. A. M. Dirac, *Proc. Roy. Soc.*, A **165**, 199 (1938).

[10] C. Brans and R. H. Dicke, *Phys. Rev.*, 124, 925 (1961) (see appendix 7).

[11] R. H. Dicke, *Phys. Rev.*, **125**, 2163 (1962) (see appendix 2).

[12] J. L. Synge, *Relativity, The General Theory*, North-Holland Publishing Co., Amsterdam. Preface (1960).

[13] R. H. Dicke, *Rev. Mod. Phys.*, **34**, 110, (1962) (see appendix 10).

[14] A. Sandage, *Astrophys. J.*, **133**, 355 (1961).

[15] F. Hoyle, *Monthly Notices Roy. Astron. Soc.*, **108** (1948) 372; 120, 256 (1960).

[16] H. Bondi and T. Gold, *Monthly Notices Roy. Astron. Soc.*, **108**, 252 (1948).

Appendix 6

Significance of Spatial Isotropy*

P. J. Peebles and R. H. Dicke

Reprinted from *The Physial Review*, Vol. 127, No. 2, 629–631, July 15, 1962

It has been suggested occasionally that the fine structure "constant" may not be a fixed number, but that it may be determined, in a manner not yet understood, by the distribution of mass in the universe. A simple point-particle picture is used to indicate the significance of this idea for the motion of free test particles. The possible generally covariant equations of motion for a point particle are considered, and it is shown that one can find a suitable model which is consistent with the observed structure independence of gravitational acceleration. However, it is indicated that such a model is not consistent with the precise observations, made by Hughes *et al.* and Drever, of the local isotropy of space. That is, with the observed structure independence of gravitational acceleration and local isotropy of space, and assuming general covariance, it seems to be necessary to rule out any appreciable variation with position in the value of the fine structure constant.

Evidence for the local isotropic nature of space has been drawn from recent discussions of nuclear magnetic resonance experiments.[1–4] This need not conflict with Mach's Principle.[5,6] However, this evidence, along with the observation that gravitational acceleration is sensibly independent of structure[7] does have an indirect bearing on the conjecture that the values of physical numbers such as the fine structure constant may be determined by the structure of the universe.[8] The connection with the observations arises when one attempts to fit such a conjecture into a generally covariant field theory of gravity.

The possibility of a variable fine structure "constant" follows from the idea that the gravitational interaction might play an important role in the structure of elementary particles,[9,10] and that Mach's principle might imply a connection between the strength of the gravitational interaction and the structure of the universe.[11,12] By this argument $\alpha = e^2/\hbar c$ might be given by the approximate equation[10]

$$\alpha^{-1} \sim \ln{(\hbar c / G m^2)}, \tag{1}$$

* This work was supported in part by research contracts with the Office of Naval Research and the U. S. Atomic Energy Commission.

where m is the mass of an elementary particle, and where G is given in the sense of a rough order of magnitude by an approximate equation of the general form

$$G^{-1} \sim \sum m_i{'}r_ic^2. \tag{2}$$

The sum is to be taken over all particles in the visible (that is, casually connected) part of the universe. A proper relativistic formulation of an equation similar to (2) has been given.[12]

Accepting for the moment the validity of these ideas, one would expect that the energy of a particle, measured with given clocks and measuring rods, depends on position. For example, with equations (1) and (2), the rate of change with position of the energy of a nucleus would be

$$dE/dx \sim (E_e/\alpha)(d\alpha/dx) \sim -\alpha E_e G(dG^{-1}/dx) \sim \alpha E_e[-G(d/dx)\sum m_i{'}r_ic^2], \tag{3}$$

where E is the total energy and E_e the electrostatic energy of the nucleus. Corrections to (3) due to the compressibility of the nucleus are not important here. Units of energy were chosen so that the energy of a particle which has no electromagnetic structure would be constant. Neglecting the very small variation in G with position, the term in square brackets in equation (3) is seen to be the gradient of the dimensionless Newtonian gravitational potential.

These ideas cannot be ruled out by the observational evidence which has been considered so far.[13] We are interested here in the problem of whether the idea of variable energy [for example, equation (3)] can fit into a generally covariant field theory of gravity consistent with the Eötvös experiment and the observations of spatial isotropy.

The problem is particularly simple if complex objects, such as atoms, are treated as point particles, where, to take account of the above conjecture, the mass of the particle is variable. The equations of motion of a point particle in general relativity are derived from the equation

$$0 = \delta \int m(g_{ij}u^iu^j)^{1/2}ds, \tag{4}$$

where $u^i = dx^i/ds$ is the velocity of the particle. If this were modified with a variable mass $m(x)$, the equation of motion would be

$$(d/ds)(mg_{ij}u^j) = \tfrac{1}{2}m(\partial g_{jk}/\partial x^i)u^ju^k + (\partial m/\partial x^i). \tag{5}$$

With the example mentioned above, the size of the second term on the right-hand side of (5) would be estimated using equation (3). Here the difference in the gravitational accelerations of different particles may be of the order of $\alpha E_e/E$ times the gravitational acceleration. The ratio E_e/E of electrostatic to total energy may be as large as 10^{-2}, so the accelerations of different particles may differ by a part in 10^4. This is at least four orders of magnitude larger than the limit set by observations.[7]

We must seek a new gravitational force field to balance the anomalous force due to variable energy. The simplest assumption is a scalar field $\varphi(x)$. The action

(4) would be modified by adding an interaction term

$$0 = \delta \int [m(x)\,(g_{ij}u^i u^j)^{1/2} + \varphi(x)]ds. \tag{6}$$

This, however, adds nothing new for the velocities u_i must satisfy

$$g_{ij}u^i u^j = 1, \tag{7}$$

and equation (6), with the constraint (7) is equivalent to equation (4), with m replaced by $m + \varphi$.

The next simplest scheme would be a vector field $f_i(\eta)$ with the action principle

$$0 = \delta \int [m(x)\,(g_{ij}u^i u^j)^{1/2} + f_i u^i]ds. \tag{8}$$

This theory is invariant against gauge transformations of $f_i(x)$. With a more realistic model for test particles, this would mean that equation (8) corresponds to a situation where $f_i(x)$ couples with a conserved quantity, such as charge or heavy-particle number. It would be possible to change the structure of the particle appreciably, and hence to alter the anomalous gravitational force associated with variable energy, without altering the force due to $f_i(x)$. It is concluded that the vector theory is of no interest for this simplified discussion of the possible gravitational fields which might interact with real particles.

The theory with a tensor field (in addition to the metric tensor) need not conflict with the Eötvös experiment. With the field h_{ij}, the only interesting scalar is $h_{ij}u^i u^j$, and the free variational principle representing an interaction with a tensor field and leading to equations of motion consistent with equation (7) is

$$0 = \delta \int [m(x)\,(g_{ij}u^i u^j)^{1/2} + \bar{m}(x)\,(h_{ij}u^i u^j)^{1/2}]ds. \tag{9}$$

Here, $m(x)$ and $\bar{m}(x)$ are masses which characterize the structure of the particle. $\bar{m}$ is a measure of the mass of the particle associated with its electromagnetic character.

Here, the path of the particle depends on its structure. However to make the theory consistent with the Eötvös experiment, it is only necessary to require that the acceleration should be sensibly independent of structure for a particle at rest on the earth. It is important that the earth is moving slowly relative to the comoving coordinate frame of the universe, the relative velocity being between 30 km/sec (the speed of the earth relative to the sun) and 300 km/sec (the supper limit determined from the approximately isotropic distribution of galactic red shifts).

In regions of space well removed from local inhomogeneities the universe may be reasonably assumed to appear very nearly isotropic, so that with appropriate coordinates, the comoving coordinate frame, the metric tensor g_{ij}, and the gravitational field h_{ij} are diagonal, with $g_{11} = g_{22} = g_{33}$ and $h_{11} = h_{22} = h_{33}$. Since the time scale for expansion of the universe is large with respect to processes we want to consider, the components of h_{ij} and g_{ij} are substantially constant. The effect on the components of h_{ij} and g_{ij} from the presence of the sun is small and will be neglected, but not the effect on the gradients of these tensors.

By appropriately redefining the fields g_{ij} and h_{ij}, and $m(x)$ and $\bar{m}(x)$, it is possible (if $m \neq 0$) to write the action (9) so that m is constant, and in the special frame mentioned above, $g_{00} = h_{00}$. Then it may be verified that if $\bar{m}(x)$ satisfied the condition

$$\frac{1}{m}\frac{\partial m}{\partial x^\alpha} = \frac{1}{2}\frac{1}{g_{00}}\frac{\partial g_{00}}{\partial x^\alpha}\left(\frac{h_{\alpha\alpha}}{g_{\alpha\alpha}} - 1\right), \tag{10}$$

(no sum on α; $\alpha = 1, 2, 3$) where the field components in this equation are supposed to be evaluated in the special coordinate frame, the gravitational acceleration of a particle at rest in this frame would be independent of m and $\bar{m}$, that is, independent of the structure of the particle.

For a particle moving with speed v with respect to this frame, accelerations of different particles may differ by the following amount, taken relative to the gravitational acceleration in the frame

$$|\delta g/g| \sim \bar{m}/m(v/c)^2\,(h_{\alpha\alpha}/g_{\alpha\alpha} - 1). \tag{11}$$

We have assumed here that $\bar{m}/m \ll 1$.

As discussed above, $\bar{m}$ is the contribution to the mass of the particle associated with its electromagnetic structure, and $\bar{m}/m = E_e/(E - E_e)$, $\bar{m}/m \lesssim 10^{-2}$. For the conditions under which the Eötvös experiment was performed $(v/c)^2 \lesssim 10^{-6}$, and by equations (3) and (10) $|1 - h_{\alpha\alpha}/g_{\alpha\alpha}| \sim 10^{-2}$, so the anomalous acceleration (11) here is less than one part in 10^{10}. This is consistent with Eötvös's limit of five parts in 10^9 on possible departures from exact structure independence of gravitational acceleration.[7]

The next step would be to use a more reasonable model for the test particle. We have considered a test particle consisting of a distribution of interacting classical fields.[14] To include equations (1) and (2) in this model, Maxwell's equations for the electromagnetic field in the particle would be suitably modified. Then, following the above example [equation (9)] we would suppose that all the fields in the particle, save the electromagnetic field, obey the usual field equations with metric tensor g_{ij}, while in the action for the electromagnetic field g_{ij} is replaced everywhere with a symmetric tensor gravitational field h_{ij}. This theory can be consistent with the results of the Eötvös experiment.

There are several observational tests of covariant field theories of gravity in which particles have variable energies. Inertial mass is not equivalent to energy in such a theory,[15] and the momentum of a particle with high laboratory energy is not related to the energy of the particle in the usual way. A most significant test is provided by the condition of spatial isotropy.[2–4]

Consider a nucleus moving relative to the special coordinate frame defined above with speed v. With coordinates chosen such that the nucleus is at rest, and the comoving coordinate frame of the universe moving in the x^3 direction, and such that the metric tensor g_{ij} has the Minkowski form, the components h_{11} and h_{33} of the tensor field are not equal,

$$|(h_{11} - h_{33})/h_{11}| \sim \alpha(v/c)^2. \tag{12}$$

We have used the conditions (3) and (10) on the components of h_{ij}.

The nucleons in the nucleus have some electromagnetic structure, so the inertial mass of a nucleon, in the point particle picture [equation (9)], is expected to have an anisotropic part in this coordinate frame. A more important effect is that the electromagnetic field equations have an anisotropic form. To estimate how this perturbs the energy levels of the nucleus, we can go to a rest coordinate frame chosen so that locally h_{ij} has the Minkowski form. By (12) the shape of the nucleus in this frame is distorted along the direction x^3, and the electrostatic energy of a nucleus may depend on orientation relative to the x^3 axis. The relative shift in energy levels belonging to different magnetic quantum numbers is approximately[14]

$$\alpha(v/c)^2 \, (\nabla c^2 q / R^3). \tag{13}$$

Here, q is the quadrupole moment, Z the atomic number, and R the radius of the nucleus. e is the charge on a proton.

The recent experiments have used Li^7, with $q \sim 2 \times 10^{-26}$ cm^2.[16] The speed of the earth relative to the special coordinate frame is expected to be at least 30 km/sec, (the speed of the earth relative to the sun), and by equation (13) the relative shift in energy levels is at least 10^{10} cps. This is larger than the experimental limit[2-4] by a factor of about 10^{10}.

It is apparent that the assumption of general covariance places a very important restriction on possible gravity theories. We have shown that it is possible to find a generally covariant theory for the motion of point particles which is consistent with the Eötvös experiment, and in which the ratios of masses of particles may vary appreciably with position. It was mentioned that this theory can be adapted to a more realistic model for physical particles. We have found from the discussion of point particles that a generally covariant theory in which particles have variable energies seems necessarily to involve at least two tensor fields. In this case, it is very difficult to make the theory consistent with the accurate observations of spatial isotropy.

It was earlier suggested by one of us (R. H. D.)[15] that the systematic discrepancy between the inertial and Q-value mass scale may be related to a variable fine structure constant. Assuming the validity of the above interpretation of the significance of the space isotropy experiments, this possibility now seems quite unlikely.

Notes and References to Appendix 6

[1] G. Cocconi and E. E. Salpeter, *Nuovo cimento*, **10**, 646 (1958).

[2] V. W. Hughes, H. G. Robinson, and V. Beltran–Lopez, *Phys. Rev. Letters* **4**, 342 (1960).

[3] C. W. Sherwin, H. Frauenfelder, E. L. Garwin, E. Luscher, S. Margulies, and R. N. Peacock, *Phys. Rev. Letters*, **4**, 399 (1960).

[4] R. W. P. Drever, *Phil. Mag.*, **6**, 683 (1961).

[5] S. T. Epstein, *Nuivo cimento*, **16**, 587 (1960).

[6] R. H. Dicke, *Phys. Rev. Letters* **7**, 359 (1961) (see appendix 1).

[7] R. V. Eötvös, *Ann. Physik* **68**, 11 (1922).

[8] R. H. Dicke, *Science*, **129**, 621 (1959).

[9] R. Arnowitt, S. Deser, and C. W. Misner, *Phys. Rev.*, **120**, 313 (1960).

[10] L. Landau, in *Niels Bohr and The Development of Physics*, edited by W. Pauli (McGraw-Hill Book Company, New York, 1955).

[11] D. W. Sciama, *Monthly Notices Roy. Astron. Soc.*, **113**, 34 (1953).

[12] C. Brans and R. H. Dicke, *Phys. Rev.*, **124**, 925 (1961) (see appendix 7).

[13] J. Peebles and R. H. Dicke (to be published) (see appendix 6).

[14] J. Peebles (to be published).

[15] R. H. Dicke, *Am. J. Phys.* **28**, 344 (1960), equation (1) of this reference can be obtained directly from the above equation (10), making use of the definition of inertial mass and energy obtained from equation (9).

[16] C. H. Townes, *Handbuch der Physik*, edited by S. Flügge (Springer–Verlag, Berlin, Germany 1958), Vol. 38, Part 1.

Appendix 7

Mach's Principle and a Relativistic Theory of Gravitation*

C. Brans† and R. H. Dicke

Reprinted from *The Physical Review*, Vol. 124, No. 3, 925–935, November 1, 1961

The role of Mach's principle in physics is discussed in relation to the equivalence principle. The difficulties encountered in attempting to incorporate Mach's principle into general relativity are discussed. A modified relativistic theory of gravitation, apparently compatible with Mach's principle, is developed.

Introduction

It is interesting that only two ideas concerning the nature of space have dominated our thinking since the time of Descartes. According to one of these pictures, space is an absolute physical structure with properties of its own. This picture can be traced from Descartes vortices[1] through the absolute space of Newton,[2] to the ether theories of the nineteenth century. The contrary view that the geometrical and inertial properties of space are meaningless for an empty space, that the physical properties of space have their origin in the matter contained therein, and that the only meaningful motion of a particle is motion relative to other matter in the universe has never found its complete expression in a physical theory. This picture is also old and can be traced from the writings of Bishop Berkeley[3] to those of Ernst Mach.[4] These ideas have found a limited expression in general relativity, but it must be admitted that, although in general relativity spatial geometries are affected by mass distributions, the geometry is not uniquely specified by the distribution. It has not yet been possible to specify boundary conditions on the field equations of general relativity which would bring the theory into accord with Mach's principle. Such boundary conditions would, among other things, eliminate all solutions without mass present.

It is necessary to remark that, according to the ideas of Mach, the inertial forces observed locally in an accelerated laboratory may be interpreted as gravitational effects having their origin in distant matter accelerated relative to the laboratory. The imperfect expression of this idea in general relativity can be seen by considering the case of a space empty except for a lone experimenter in his laboratory. Using the traditional asymptotically Minkowskian coordinate system fixed relative to the laboratory, and assuming a normal laboratory of small mass, its effect on the metric is minor and can be considered in the weak-field approximation. The

* Supported in part by research contracts with the U.S. Atomic Energy Commission and the Office of Naval Research.

† National Science Foundation Fellow; now at Loyola University, New Orleans, Louisiana.

observer would, according to general relativity, observe normal behavior of his apparatus in accordance with the usual laws of physics. However, also according to general relativity, the experimenter could set his laboratory rotating by leaning out of a window and firing his 22-caliber rifle tangentially. Thereafter the delicate gyroscope in the laboratory would continue to point in a direction nearly fixed relative to the direction of motion of the rapidly receding bullet. The gyroscope would rotate relative to the walls of the laboratory. Thus, from the point of view of Mach, the tiny, almost massless, very distant bullet seems to be more important than the massive, nearby walls of the laboratory in determining inertial coordinate frames and the orientation of the gyroscope.[5] It is clear that what is being described here is more nearly an absolute space in the sense of Newton rather than a physical space in the sense of Berkeley and Mach.

The above example poses a problem for us. Apparently, we may assume one of at least three things:

1. that physical space has intrinsic geometrical and inertial properties beyond those derived from the matter contained therein;

2. that the above example may be excluded as nonphysical by some presently unknown boundary condition on the equations of general relativity;

3. that the above physical situation is not correctly described by the equations of general relativity.

These various alternatives have been discussed previously. Objections to the first possibility are mainly philosophical and, as stated previously, go back to the time of Bishop Berkeley. A common inheritance of all present-day physicists from Einstein is an appreciation of the concept of relativity of motion.

As the universe is observed to be nonuniform, it would appear to be difficult to specify boundary conditions which would have the effect of prohibiting unsuitable mass distributions relative to the laboratory *arbitrarily placed*; for could not a laboratory be built near a massive star? Should not the presence of this massive star contribute to the inertial reaction?

The difficulty is brought into sharper focus by considering the laws of physics, including their quantitative aspects, inside a static massive spherical shell. It is well known that the interior Schwarzchild solution is flat and can be expressed in a coordinate system Minkowskian in the interior. Also, according to general relativity all Minkowskian coordinate systems are equivalent and the mass and radius of the spherical shell have no discernible effects upon the laws of physics as they are observed in the interior. Apparently the spherical shell does not contribute in any discernible way to inertial effects in the interior. What would happen if the mass of the shell were decreased, or its radius increased without limit? It might be remarked also that Komar[6] has attempted, without success, to find suitable boundary- and initial-value conditions for general relativity which would bring into evidence Mach's principles.

The third alternative is the subject of this paper. Actually the objectives of this paper are more limited than the formulation of a theory in comple accord with Mach's principle. Such a program would consist of two parts, the formulation of a suitable field theory and the formulation of suitable boundary- and initial-value conditions for the theory which would make the space geometry depend uniquely upon the matter distribution. This latter part of the problem is treated only partially.

At the end of the last section we shall briefly return again to the problem of the rotating laboratory.

A principle as sweeping as that of Mach, having its origins in matters of philosophy, can be described in the absence of a theory in a qualitative way only. A model of a theory incorporating elements of Mach's principle has been given by Sciama.[7] From simple dimensional arguments[8,9] as well as the discussion of Scaima, it has appeared that, with the assumption of validity of Mach's principle, the gravitational constant G is related to the mass distribution in a uniform expanding universe in the following way:

$$GM/Rc^2 \sim 1. \tag{1}$$

Here M stands for the finite mass of the visible (i.e., casually related) universe, and R stands for the radius of the boundary of the visible universe.

The physical ideas behind equation (1) have been given in references 7–9 and can be summarized easily. As stated before, according to Mach's principle the only meaningful motion is that relative to the rest of the matter in the universe, and the inertial reaction experienced in a laboratory accelerated relative to the distant matter of the universe may be interpreted equivalently as a gravitational force acting on a fixed laboratory due to the presence of distant accelerated matter.[7] This interpretation of the inertial reaction carries with it an interesting implication. Consider a test body falling toward the sun. In a coordinate system so chosen that the object is not accelerating, the gravitational pull of the sun may be considered as balanced by another gravitational pull, the inertial reaction.[8] Note that the balance is not disturbed by a doubling of all gravitational forces. Thus the acceleration is determined by the mass distribution in the universe, but is independent of the strength of gravitational interactions. Designating the mass of the sun by m_s and its distance by r enables the acceleration to be expressed according to Newton as $a = Gm_s/r^2$ or, from dimensional arguments, in terms of the mass distribution as $a \sim mRc^2/Mr^2$. Combining the two expressions given equation (1).

This relation has significance in a rough order-of-magnitude manner only, but it suggests that either the ratio of M to R should be fixed by the theory, or alternatively that the gravitational constant observed locally should be variable and determined by the mass distribution about the point in question. The first of these two alternatives is of course, in part, simply the limitation of mass distribution which it might be hoped would result from some boundary condition on the field equations of general relativity. The second alternative is not compatible with the "strong principle of equivalence"[10] and general relativity. The reasons for this will be discussed below.

If the inertial reaction may be interpreted as a gravitational force due to distant accelerated matter, it might be expected that the locally observed values of the inertial masses of particles would depend upon the distribution of matter about the point in question. It should be noted, however, that there is a fundamental ambiguity in a statement of this type, for there is no direct way in which the mass of a particle such as an electron can be compared with that of another at a different space-time point. Mass ratios can be compared at different points, but not masses. On the other hand, gravitation provides another characteristic mass

$$(\hbar c/G)^{1/2} = 2.16 \times 10^{-5}\,g, \tag{2}$$

and the mass ratio, the dimensionless number

$$m(G/\hbar c)^{1/2} \cong 5 \times 10^{-23},\tag{3}$$

provides an unambiguous measure of the mass of an electron which can be compared at different space-time points.

It should also be remarked that statements such as "$\hbar$ and c are the same at all space-time points" are in the same way meaningless within the same context until a method of measurement is prescribed. In fact, it should be noted that $\hbar$ and c may be defined to be constant. A set of physical "constants" may be defined as constant if they cannot be combined to form one or more dimensionless numbers. The necessity for this limitation is obvious, for a dimensionless number is invariant under a transformation of units and the question of the constancy of such dimensionless numbers is to be settled, not by definition, but by measurements. A set of such independent physical constants which are constant by definition is "complete" if it is impossible to include another without generating dimensionless numbers.

It should be noted that if the number, equation (3), should vary with position and $\hbar$ and c are defined as constant, then either m or G, or both, could vary with position. There is no fundamental difference between the alternatives of constant mass or constant G. However, one or the other may be more convenient, for the formal structure of the theory would, in a superficial way, be quite different for the two cases.

To return to equation (3), the odd size of this dimensionless number has often been noticed as well as its apparent relation to the large dimensionless numbers of astrophysics. The apparent relation of the square of the reciprocal of this number [equation (3)] to the age of the universe expressed as a dimensionless number in atomic time units and the square root of the mass of the visible portion of the universe expressed in proton mass units suggested to Dirac[11] a causal connection that would lead to the value of equation (3) changing with time. The significance of Dirac's hypothesis from the standpoint of Mach's principle has been discussed.[8]

Dirac postulated a detailed cosmological model based on these numerical coincidences. This has been criticized on the grounds that it goes well beyond the empirical data upon which it is based.[8] Also in another publication by one of us (R. H. D.), it will be shown that it gives results not in accord with astrophysical observations examined in the light of modern stellar evolutionary theory.

On the other hand, it should be noted that a large dimensionless physical constant such as the reciprocal of equation (3) must be regarded as either determined by nature in a completely capricious fashion or else are related to some other large number derived from nature. In any case, it seems unreasonable to attept to derive a number like 10^{23} from theory as a purely mathematical number involving factors such as $4\pi/3$.

It is concluded therefore, that although the detailed structure of Dirac's cosmology cannot be justified by the weak empirical evidence on which it is based, the more general conclusion that the number [equation (3)] varies with time has a more solid basis.

If, in line with the interpretation of Mach's principle being developed, the dimensionless mass ratio given by equation (3) should depend upon the matter distribution in the universe, with h and c constant by definition, either the mass m or the gravitational constant, or both, must vary. Although these are alternative descriptions of the same physical situation, the formal structure of the theory would be very different for the two cases. Thus, for example, it can be easily shown that uncharged spinless particles whose masses are position dependent no longer move on geodesics of the metric. (See Appendix) thus, the definition of the metric tensor is different for the two cases. The two metric tensors are connected by a conformal transformation.

The arbitrariness in the metric tensor which results from the indefiniteness in the choice of units of measure raises questions about the physical significance of Riemannian geometry in relativity.[12] In particular the 14 invariants which characterize the space are generally not invariant under a conformal transformation interpreted as a redefinition of the metric tensor in the *same* space.[13] Matters are even worse, for a more general redefinition of the units of measure can be used to reduce all 14 invariants to zero. It should be said that these remarks should not be interpreted as casting doubt on the correctness or usefulness of Riemannian geometry in relativity, but rather that each such geometry is but a particular representation of the theory. It would be expected that the physical content of the theory should be contained in the invariants of the group of position-dependent transformations of units and coordinate transformations. The usual invariants of Riemannian geometry are not invariants under this wider group.

In general relativity the representation is one in which units are chosen so that atoms are described as having physical properties independent of location. It is assumed that this choice is possible!

In accordance with the above, a particular choice of units is made with the realization that the choice is arbitrary and without an invariant significance. The theoretical structure appears to be simpler if one defines the inertial masses of elementary particles to be constant and permits the gravitational constant to vary. It should be noted that this is possible only if the mass ratios of elementary particles are constant. There may be reasonable doubt about this.[9,10] On the other hand, it would be expected that such quantities as particle mass ratios or the fine-structure constant, if they depend upon mass distributions in the universe, would be much less sensitive in their dependence[9] rather than the number given by equation (3) and their variation could be neglected in a first crude theory. Also it should be remarked that the requirements of the approximate constancy of the ratio of inertial to passive gravitational mass,[14] and the extremely stringent requirement of spatial isotropy,[15] impose conditions so severe that it has been found to be difficult, if not impossible, to construct a satisfactory theory with a variable fine-structure constant.

It should be emphasized that the above argument involving the large dimensionless numbers, equation (3), does not concern Mach's principle directly, but that Mach's principle and the assumption of a gravitational "constant" depend upon mass distributions gives a reasonable explanation for varying "constants."

It would be expected that both nearby and distant matter should contribute to the inertial reaction experienced locally. If the theory were linear, which one does not expect, equation (1) would suggest that it is the reciprocal of the gravitational constant which is determined locally as a linear superposition of contributions from the matter in the universe which is casually connected to the point in question. This can be expressed in a somewhat symbolic equation:

$$G^{-1} \sim \sum_i (m_i/r_i c^2), \qquad (4)$$

where the sum is over all the matter which can contribute to the inertial reaction. This equation can be given an exact meaning only after a theory has been constructed. Equation (4) is also a relation from Sciama's theory.

It is necessary to say a few words about the equivalence principle as it is used in general relativity and as it relates to Mach's principle. As it enters general relativity, the equivalence principle is more than the assumption of the local equivalence of a gravitational force and an acceleration. Actually, in general relativity it is assumed that the laws of physics, including numerical content (i.e., dimensionless physical constants), as observed locally in a freely falling laboratory, are independent of the location in time or space of the laboratory. This is a statement of the "strong equivalence principle."[9,10] The interpretation of Mach's principle being developed here is obviously incompatible with strong equivalence. The local equality of all gravitational accelerations (to the accuracy of present experiments) is the "weak equivalence principle." It should be noted that it is the "weak equivalence principle" that receives strong experimental support from the Eötvös experiment.

Before attempting to formulate a theory of gravitation which is more satisfactory from the standpoint of Mach's principle than general relativity, the physical ideas outlined above, and the assumptions being made, will be summarized:

1. An approach to Mach's principle which attempts, with boundary conditions, to allow only those mass distributions which produce the "correct" inertial reaction seems foredoomed, for there do exist large localized masses in the universe (e.g., white dwarf stars) and a laboratory could, in principle, be constructed near such a mass. Also it appears to be possible to modify the mass distribution. For example, a massive concrete spherical shell could be constructed with the laboratory in its interior.

2. The contrary view is that locally observed inertial reactions depend upon the mass distribution of the universe about the point of observation and consequently the quantitative aspects of locally observed physical laws (as expressed in the physical "constants") are position dependent.

3. It is possible to reduce the variation of physical "constants" required by this interpretation of Mach's principle to that of a single parameter, the gravitational "constant."

4. The separate but related problem posed by the existence of very large dimensionless numbers representing quantitative aspects of physical laws is clarified by noting that these large numbers involve G and that they are of the same order of magnitude as the large numbers characterizing the size and mass distribution of the universe.

5. The "strong principle of equivalence" upon which general relativity rests is incompatible with these ideas. However, it is only the "weak principle" which is directly supported by the very precise experiments of Eötvös.

A Theory of Gravitation Based on a Scalar Field in a Riemannian Geometry

The theory to be developed represents a generalization of general relativity. It is not a completely geometrical theory of gravitation, as gravitational effects are described by a scalar field in a Riemannian manifold. Thus, the gravitational effects are in part geometrical and in part due to a scalar interaction. There is a formal connection between this theory and that of Jordan,[16] but there are differences and the physical interpretation is quite different. For example, the aspect of mass creation[17] in Jordan's theory is absent from this theory.

In developing this theory we start with the "weak principle of equivalence." The great accuracy of the Eötvös experiment suggests that the motion of uncharged test particles in this theory should be, as in general relativity, a geodesic in the four-dimensional manifold.

With the assumption that only the gravitational "constant" (or active gravitational masses) vary with position, the laws of physics (exclusive of gravitation) observed in a freely falling laboratory should be unaffected by the rest of the universe as long as self-gravitational fields are negligible. The theory should be constructed in such a way as to exhibit this effect.

If the gravitational "constant" is to vary, it should be a function of some scalar field variable. The contracted metric tensor is a constant and devoid of interest. The scalar curvature and the other scalars formed from the curvature tensor are also devoid of interest as they contain gradients of the metric tensor components, and fall off more rapidly than r^{-1} from a mass source. Thus such scalars are determined primarily by nearby mass distributions rather than by distant matter.

As the scalars of general relativity are not suitable, a new scalar field is introduced. The primary function of this field is the determination of the local value of the gravitational constant.

In order to generalize general relativity, we start with the usual variational principle of general relativity from which the equations of motion of matter and non-gravitational fields are obtained as well as the Einstein field equation, namely,[18]

$$0 = \delta \int [R + (16\pi G/c^4)L](-g)^{1/2}d^4x. \tag{5}$$

Here, R is the scalar curvature and L is the Lagrangian density of matter including all nongravitational fields.

In order to generalize equation (5) it is first divided by G, and a Lagrangian density of a scalar field ϕ is added inside the bracket. G is assumed to be a function of ϕ. Remembering the discussion in connection with equation (4), it would be reasonable to assume that G^{-1} varies as ϕ, for then a simple wave equation for ϕ with a scalar matter density as source would give an equation roughly the same as (4).

The required generalization of equation (6) is clearly

$$0 = \delta \int [\phi R + (16\pi/c^4) L - \omega(\phi_{,i}\phi^{,i}/\phi)](-g)^{1/2}d^4x. \tag{6}$$

Here ϕ plays a role analogous to G^{-1} and will have the dimensions $ML^{-3}T^2$. The third term is the usual Lagrangian density of a scalar field, and the scalar in the denominator has been introduced to permit the constant ω to be dimensionless. In any sensible theory ω must be of the general order of magnitude of unity.

It should be noted that the term involving the Lagrangian density of matter in equation (6) is identical with that in equation (5). Thus the equations of motion of matter in a given externally determined metric field are the same as in general relativity. The difference between the two theories lies in the gravitational field equations which determine g_{ij}, rather than in the equations of motion in a given metric field.

It is evident, therefore, that, as in general relativity, the energy-momentum tensor of matter must have a vanishing covariant divergence,

where
$$T^{ij}{}_{;j} = 0, \tag{7}$$
$$T^{ij} = [2/(-g)^{1/2}] (\partial/\partial g_{ij}) [(-g)^{1/2}L]. \tag{8}$$

It is assumed that L does not depend explicitly upon derivatives of g_{ij}.

Jordan's theory has been criticized by Fierz[19] on the grounds that the introduction of matter into the theory required further assumptions concerning the standards of length and time. Further, the mass creation aspects of this theory and the nonconservation of the energy-momentum tensor raise serious questions about the significance of the energy-momentum tensor. To make it clear that this objection cannot be raised against this version of the theory, we hasten to point out that L is assumed to be the normal Lagrangian density of matter, a function of matter variables and of g_{ij} only, *not* a function of ϕ. It is a well-known result that for *any* reasonable metric field distribution g_{ij} (a distribution which need not be a solution of the field equations of g_{ij}), the matter equations of motion, obtained by varying matter variables in equation (6), are such that equation (7) is satisfied with T^{ij} defined by equation (8). Thus equation (7) is satisfied and this theory does not contain a mass creation principle.

The wave equation for ϕ is obtained in the usual way by varying ϕ and $\phi_{,i}$ in equation (6). This gives

$$2\omega\phi^{-1}\Box\phi - (\omega/\phi^2) \phi^{,i}\phi_{,i} + R = 0. \tag{9}$$

Here the generally covariant d'Alembertian $\Box$ is defined to be the covariant divergence of $\phi^{,i}$:

$$\Box\phi = \phi^{,i}{}_{;i} = (-g)^{-1/2}[(-g)^{1/2}\phi^{,i}]{}_{,i}. \tag{10}$$

From the form of equation (9), it is evident that ϕR and the Lagrangian density of ϕ serves as the source term for the generation of ϕ waves. Remarkably enough, as will be shown below, this equation can be transformed so as to make the source term appear as the contracted energy-momentum tensor of matter alone. Thus, in accordance with the requirements of Mach's principle, ϕ has as its sources the matter distribution in space.

By varying the components of the metric tensor and their first derivatives in equation (6), the field equations for the metric field are obtained. This is the analog of the Einstein field equation and is

$$R_{ij} - \tfrac{1}{2}g_{ij}R = (8\pi\phi^{-1}/c^4)T_{ij}$$
$$+ (\omega/\phi^2) (\phi_{,i}\phi_{,j} - \tfrac{1}{2}g_{ij}\phi_{,k}\phi^{,k})$$
$$+ \phi^{-1}(\phi_{,i;j} - g_{ij} \Box \phi). \tag{11}$$

The left side of equation (11) is completely familar and needs no comment. Note that the first term on the right is the usual source term of general relativity, but with the variable gravitational coupling parameter ϕ^{-1}. Note also that the second term is the energy-momentum tensor of the scalar field, also coupled with the gravitational coupling ϕ^{-1}. The third term is foreign and results from the presence of second derivatives of the metric tensor in R in equation (6). These second derivatives are eliminated by integration by parts to give a divergence and the extra terms. It should be noted that when the first term dominates the right side of equation (11), the equation differs from Einstein's field equation by the presence of a variable gravitational constant only.

While the "extra" terms in equation (12) may at first seem strange, their role is essential. They are needed if equation (7) is to be consistent with equation (9) and (11). This can be seen by multiplying equation (11) by ϕ and then taking the covariant divergence of the resulting equation. The divergence of these two terms cancels the term $\phi_{,i}R_j{}^i = \phi^{,i}R_{ji}$. To show this, use is made of the wellknown property of the full curvature tensor that it serves as a commutator for two successive gradient operations applied to an arbitrary vector.

If equation (11) is contracted there results

$$-R = (8\pi\phi^{-1}/c^4)T - (\omega/\phi^2)\phi_{,k}\phi^{,k} - 3\phi^{-1}\Box\phi. \tag{12}$$

Equation (12) can be combined with equation (9) to give a new wave equation for ϕ[20]:

$$\Box\phi = [8\pi/(3 + 2\omega)c^4]T. \tag{13}$$

With the sign convention

$$ds^2 = g_{ij}dx^idx^j \text{ and } g_{00} < 0,$$

for a fluid

$$T_{ij} = -(p + \epsilon)u_iu_j + pg_{ij}, \tag{14}$$

so that

$$T = -\epsilon + 3p, \tag{15}$$

where ϵ is the energy density of the matter in comoving coordinates and p is the pressure in the fluid. With this sign convention and ω positive, the contribution to ϕ from a local mass is positive. Note, however, that there is no direct electromagnetic contribution to T, as the contracted energy-momentum tensor of an electromagnetic field is identically zero. However, bound electromagnetic energy does contribute indirectly through the stress terms in other fields, the stresses being necessary to confine the electromagnetic field.[21] In conclusion, ω must be positive if the contribution to the inertial reaction from nearby matter is to be positive.

The Weak Field Approximation

An approximate solution to equations (11) and (13) which is of first order in matter mass densities is now obtained. This weak-field solution plays the same important role that the corresponding solution fills in general relativity.

As in general relativity the metric tensor is written as

$$g_{ij} = \eta_{ij} + h_{ij}, \tag{16}$$

where η_{ij} is the Minkowskian metric tensor

$$\eta_{00} = -1, \qquad \eta_{\alpha\alpha} = 1, \qquad \alpha = 1, 2, 3. \qquad (17)$$

h_{ij} is computed to the linear first approximation only. In similar fashion let $\phi = \phi_0 + \xi$, where ϕ_0 is a constant and is to be computed to first order in mass densities.

The weak-field solution to equation (13) is computed first. In this equation g_{ij} may be replaced by η_{ij}:

$$\Box\phi = \Box\xi = \frac{1}{(-g)^{1/2}}[(-g)^{1/2}g^{ij}\xi_{,i}]_{,j} = \nabla^2\xi - \frac{\partial^2\xi}{\partial t^2} = \frac{8\pi T}{(3+2\omega)c^4}. \qquad (18)$$

It is evident that a retarded-time solution to Eq. (18) can be written as

$$\xi = -[2/(3+2\omega)]\int Td^3x/rc^4, \qquad (19)$$

where T is to be evaluated at the retarded time.

The weak-field solution to equation (11) is obtained in a manner similar to that of general relativity by introducing a coordinate condition that simplifies the equation. As a preliminary step let

$$\gamma_{ij} = h_{ij} - \tfrac{1}{2}\eta_{ij}h, \qquad (20)$$

$$\sigma_i = \gamma_{ij,k}\eta^{jk}.$$

Equation (11) can be written to first order in h_{ij} and ξ as

$$-\tfrac{1}{2}\{\Box\gamma_{ij} - \sigma_{i,j} - \sigma_{j,i} + \eta_{ij}\sigma_{k,l}\eta^{kl}\} = [\xi_{,i,j} - \eta_{ij}\Box\xi]\phi_0^{-1} + \frac{8\pi}{c^4}\phi_0^{-1}T_{ij}. \qquad (21)$$

Equation (21) can now be simplified by introducing the four coordinate conditions

$$\sigma_i = \xi_{,i}\phi_0^{-1}, \qquad (22)$$

and the notation

$$\alpha_{ij} = \gamma_{ij} - \eta_{ij}\xi\phi_0^{-1}. \qquad (23)$$

Equation (21) then becomes

$$\Box\alpha_{ij} = -(16\pi/c^4)\phi_0^{-1}T_{ij}, \qquad (24)$$

with the retarded-time solution

$$\alpha_{ij} = (4\phi_0^{-1}/c^4)\int(T_{ij}/r)d^3x. \qquad (25)$$

From equations (20) and (23),

$$h_{ij} = \alpha_{ij} - \tfrac{1}{2}\eta_{ij}\alpha - \eta_{ij}\xi\phi_0^{-1}. \qquad (26)$$

Thus

$$h_{ij} = \frac{4\phi_0^{-1}}{c^4}\int\frac{T_{ij}}{r}d^3x - \frac{4\phi_0^{-1}}{c^4}\left(\frac{1+\omega}{3+2\omega}\right)\eta_{ij}\int\frac{T}{r}d^3x. \qquad (27)$$

For a stationary mass point of mass M these equations become

$$\phi = \phi_0 + \xi = \phi_0 + 2M/(3 + 2\omega)c^2 r, \tag{28}$$

$$g_{00} = \eta_{00} + h_{00} = -1 + (2M\phi_0^{-1}/rc^2)\,[1 + 1/(3 + 2\omega)],$$

$$g_{\alpha\alpha} = 1 + (2M\phi_0^{-1}/rc^2)\,[1 - 1/(3 + 2\omega)], \qquad \alpha = 1, 2, 3, \tag{29}$$

$$g_{ij}{}^m = 0, \qquad i \neq j.$$

The above weak-field solution is sufficiently accurate to discuss the gravitational red shift and the deflection of light. However, to discuss the rotation of the perihelion of Mercury's orbit requires a solution good to the second approximation for g_{00}.

The gravitational red shift is determined by g_{00} which also determines the gravitational weight of a body. Thus, there is no anomaly in the red shift. The strange factor $(4 + 2\omega)/(3 + 2\omega)$ in g_{00} is simply absorbed into the definition of the gravitational constant

$$G_0 = \phi_0^{-1}(4 + 2\omega)\,(3 + 2\omega)^{-1}. \tag{29a}$$

On the other hand, there is an anomaly in the deflection of light. This is determined, not by g_{00} alone, but by the ratio $g_{\alpha\alpha}/g_{00}$. It is easily shown that the light deflection computed from general relativity differs from the value in this theory by the above factor. Thus, the light deflection computed from this theory is

$$\delta\theta = (4G_0M/Rc^2)[(3 + 2\omega)/(4 + 2\omega)], \tag{30}$$

where R is the closest approach distance of the light ray to the sun of mass M. It differs from the general relativity value by the factor in brackets. The accuracy of the light deflection observations is too poor to set any useful limit to the size of ω.

On the contrary, there is fair accuracy in the observation of the perihelion rotation of the orbit of Mercury and this does serve to set a limit to the size of ω. In order to discuss the perihelion rotation, an exact solution for a static mass point will be written.

Static Spherically Symmetric Field about a Point Mass[22]

Expressing the line element in isotropic form gives

$$ds^2 = -e^{2\alpha}\,dt^2 + e^{2\beta}[dr^2 + r^2(d\theta^2 + \sin^2\theta\,d\phi^2)], \tag{31}$$

where α and β are functions of r only. For $\omega > \frac{3}{2}$ the general vacuum solution can be written in the form

$$e^{2\alpha} = e^{2\alpha_0}[(1 - B/r)/(1 + B/r)]^{2/\lambda},$$

$$e^{2\beta} = e^{2\beta_0}(1 + B/r)^4[(1 - B/r)/(1 + B/r)]^{2[(\lambda - C - 1)/\lambda]}, \tag{32}$$

$$\phi = \phi_0[(1 - B/r)/(1 + B/r)]^{-C/\lambda},$$

where

$$\lambda = [(C + 1)^2 - C(1 - \tfrac{1}{2}\omega C)]^{1/2}, \tag{33}$$

and α_0, β_0, ϕ_0, B, and C are arbitrary constants. It may be seen by substitution of equations (31) and (32) into equations (13) and (11) that this is the static solution for spherical symmetry when $T_{ij} = 0$.

To discuss the perihelion rotation of a planet about the sun requires a specification of the arbitrary constants in equation (32) in such a way that this solution agrees in the weak-field limit (first order in $M/(c^2 r \phi_0)$) with the previously obtained solution, equations (28) and (29). It may be easily verified that the appropriate choice of constants is

ϕ_0 given by equation (29a);

$\alpha_0 = \beta_0 = 0$,

$C \cong -1/(2 + \omega)$,

$$B \cong (M/2c^2\phi_0)[(2\omega + 4)/(2\omega + 3)]^{1/2}, \tag{34}$$

with λ given by equation (33).

Remembering the previous disucssion of Mach's principle, it is clear that the asymptotic Minkowskian character of this solution makes sense only if there is matter at great distance. Second, the matching of the solution to the weak-field solution is permissible only if the sun is a suitable mass distribution for the weak-field approximation. Namely, the field generated by the sun must be everywhere small, including the interior of the sun. With this assumption, the solution, equations (31), (32), (33), and (34), is valid for the sun. It does not, however, justify its use for a point mass.

The question might be raised as to whether a matching of solutions, accurate to first order only in $M/(\phi_0 c^2 r)$, has a validity to the second order. It should be noted, however, that this matching condition is sufficient to assign sufficiently accurate values to all the adjustable parameters in equations (32) except λB, and that we do not demand that λB be determined in terms of an integration over the matter distribution of the sun; it is determined from the observed periods of the planetary motion.

With the above solution, it is a simple matter to calculate the perihelion rotation. The labor is reduced if $e^{2\alpha}$ is carried only to second order in $M/(c^2 r \phi_0)$, and $e^{2\beta}$ to first order. The result of this calculation is that the relativistic perihelion rotation rate of a planetary orbit is

$$[(4 + 3\omega)/(6 + 3\omega)] \times \text{(value of general relativity)}. \tag{35}$$

This is a useful result as it sets a limit on permissible values of the constant ω. If it be assumed that the observed relativistic perihelion rotation agrees with an accuracy of 8 per cent or less with the computed result of general relativity, it is necessary for ω in equation (35) to satisfy the inequality

$$\omega \geqslant 6. \tag{36}$$

The observed relativistic perihelion rotation of Mercury (after subtracting off planetary perturbations and other effects presumed known) is $42.6'' \pm 0.9''/$ century.[23] For $\omega = 6$, the computed relativistic perihelion rotation rate is $39.4''$. The difference of $3.2''$ of arc per century is 3.3 times the formal probable error. It should also be remarked that Clemence[24] has shown that if some recent data on the general precession constant and the masses of Venus and the Earth–Moon system are adopted, the result is an increase in the discrepancy to $3.7''$ while decreasing the formal probable error by a factor of 2.

The formal probable error is thus substantially less than 3.2″ arc, but it may be reasonable to allow this much to take account of systematic errors in observations and future modification of observations, adopted masses, and orbit parameters. Apparently there are many examples in celestial mechanics of quantities changing by substantially more than the formal probable errors. Thus, for example, the following is a list of values which have been assigned to the reciprocal of Saturn's mass (in units of the sun's reciprocal mass) by authors at various times:

$$M^{-1} = 3501.6 \pm 0.8, \text{ Bessel (1833) from the motion of Saturn's moon Titan;}$$
$$= 3494.8 \pm 0.3, \text{ Jeffrey (1954) and G. Struve (1924–37) (Titan);}$$
$$= 3502.2 \pm 0.53, \text{ Hill (1895) Saturn's perturbations of Jupiter;}$$
$$= 3497.64 \pm 0.27, \text{ Hertz (1953) Saturn's perturbations of Jupiter;}$$
$$= 3499.7 \pm 0.4, \text{ Clemence (1960) Saturn's perturbations of Jupiter.}$$

While this example may be atypical, it does suggest that considerable caution be used in judging errors in celestial mechanics.

Mach's Principle

A complete analysis of Mach's principle in relation to the present scalar theory will not be attempted here. However, because of the motivation of this theory by Mach's principle, it is desirable to give a brief discussion. Having formulated the desired field equations, it remains to establish initial-value and boundary conditions to bring the theory in accord with Mach's principle. This will not be attempted in a general way, but in connection with special problems only.

The qualitative discussion in the Introduction suggested that for a static mass shell of radius R and mass M, the gravitational constant in its interior should satisfy the relation

$$GM/Rc^2 \sim 1. \tag{37}$$

Equivalently

$$\phi \sim M/Rc^2. \tag{38}$$

It may be noted that in a flat space, with the boundary condition that $\phi = 0$ at infinity, equation (13) has as a solution for the interior $r < R$

$$\phi = 2M/(3 + 2\omega)Rc^2. \tag{39}$$

This is a hopeful sign and bodes well for Mach's principle within the framework of this theory. One should not be misled by this simple result, however. There are several factors which invalidate equation (39) as a quantitative result. First, space is not flat, but is warped by the presence of the mass shell. Second, the asymptotic zero boundary condition may be impossible for the exact static solution to the field equation. Third, it may be impossible to construct such a static massive shell in a universe empty except for the shell, without giving matter nonphysical properties. This third point is not meant to imply a practical limitation of real materials, but rather a fundamental limitation on the stress-energy tensor of matter. In this connection it should be noted that if equation (37) is to be satisfied, independent of the size and mass of the shell, the gravitationally induced stresses in the shell are enormous, of the order of magnitude of the energy density of the spherical shell. It is not possible to reduce the stress by decreasing M or increasing R, as the resulting change in the gravitational constant compensates for the change. We ignore here the above third point and assume for the moment that such a shell can be constructed in principle.

To turn now to the massive static shell, consider first the solution to the field equations in the exterior region, $r > R$. This solution is encompassed in the general solution equations (32) and (33). Note that the boundary condition

$$\phi \to 0 \quad \text{as} \quad r \to \infty \tag{40}$$

is not possible.

On the other hand, it is possible to change the sign in the brackets in equation (32) and absorb the complex factor into the constant before the bracket. These equations may then be assumed to hold for $r < B$ rather than for $r > B$ as in equation (32). The equations now have the form

$$e^{2\alpha} = e^{2\alpha_0}[(B/r - 1)/(B/r + 1)]^{2/\lambda},$$
$$e^{2\beta} = e^{2\beta_0}[1 + B/r]^4[(B/r - 1)/(B/r+1)]^{2[(\lambda-C-1)/\lambda]}, \tag{41}$$
$$\phi = \phi_0[(B/r - 1)/(B/r + 1)]^{C/\lambda}.$$

It may be noted that this solution, interesting for $r \to R$ and $\lambda > 0$ only, results in space closure at the radius $r = B$ provided

$$(\lambda - C - 1)/\lambda > 0. \tag{42}$$

In similar fashion at the closure radius, $\phi \to 0$, provided $C > 0$.

Equations (36) and (33) require that

$$C > 2/\omega. \tag{43}$$

That this boundary condition is appropriate to Mach's principle can be seen by an application of Green's theorem. Introduce a Green's function η satisfying

$$\Box \eta = (-g)^{-1/2}[(-g)^{1/2}g^{ij}\eta,_j],_i = (-g)^{-1/2}\delta^4(x - x_0), \tag{44}$$

also

$$\Box \phi = [8\pi/(3 + 2\omega)c^4]T. \tag{45}$$

Combining equations (44) and (45) after the appropriate multiplications gives

$$[(-g)^{1/2}g^{ij}(\eta\phi,_i - \phi\eta,_i)],_j = (-g)^{1/2}[8\pi/(3 + 2\omega)c^4]T\eta - \phi\delta^4(x-x_0). \tag{46}$$

It is assumed that η is an "advanced-wave" solution to equation (44), i.e., $\eta = 0$ for all time future to t_0. The condition given by equation (42) implies a finite coordinate time for light to propagate from the radius B to R, the radius of the shell, hence to any interior point x_0.

Integrate equation (46) over the interior of the closed space ($r < B$) between the time $t_2 > t_0$ and the space like surface S_1 so chosen that the η wave starts out at the radius $r = B$ at times lying on this surface and that the normal to the surface at $r = B$ has no component in the r direction. The integral of the left side of equation (46), after conversion to a surface integral, vanishes, for η and η_0 both vanish on t_2, and both ϕ and $\phi,_i$ vanish on S_1 at $r = B$, with $i \neq 1$.

The integral over the right side of equation (46) yields

$$\phi(x_0) = [8\pi/(3 + 2\omega)c^4]\int \eta T(-g)^{1/2}d^4x, \tag{47}$$

or

$$\phi(x_0) \sim M/Rc^2. \tag{47a}$$

Note that this equation states that ϕ at the point x_0 is determined by an integral over the mass distribution, with each mass element contributing a wavelet which propagates to the point x_0. This is just the interpretation of Mach's principle desired.

Cosmology

A physically more interesting problem to discuss from the standpoint of Mach's principle is the cosmological model derived from this theory. It will be recalled that the assumption of a uniform and isotropic space is supported to some extent by the observations of galaxy distribution. The kinematics of the comoving coordinate system is completely free of dynamical consideration. In spherical coordinates, a form of the line element is

$$ds^2 = -dt^2 + a^2(t)[dr^2/(1 - \lambda r^2) + r^2(d\theta^2 + \sin^2\theta d\phi^2)], \tag{48}$$

with $\lambda = +1$ for a closed space, $\lambda = -1$ for open, and $\lambda = 0$ for a flat space, and where $r < 1$ for the closed space. The Hubble age associated with the rate of expansion of the universe and the galactic red shift is $a/\dot{a} = a/(da/dt)$.

The subsitution

$$r = \sin\chi \text{ (closed space, } \lambda = +1)$$

or

$$r = \sinh\chi \text{ (open space, } \lambda = -1) \tag{49}$$

simplifies the expression for line element somewhat:

$$ds^2 = -dt^2 + a^2[d\chi^2 + \sin^2\chi(d\theta + \sin^2\theta\, d\phi^2)] \text{ (closed space).} \tag{50}$$

The most interesting case physically seems to be the closed universe.

Using equation (50) for interval and writing the (0, 0) component of equation (11),

$$R_0{}^0 - \tfrac{1}{2}R = -(3/a^2)(\dot{a}^2 \pm 1)$$

$$(+, \text{ space closed}; -, \text{ space open})$$

$$= \frac{8\pi\phi^{-1}}{c^4} T_0{}^0 - \frac{\omega}{2\phi^2}\dot{\phi}^2 + 3\frac{\dot{a}}{a}\frac{\dot{\phi}}{\phi}. \tag{51}$$

Assuming negligible pressure in the universe we have $-T = -T_0{}^0 = +\rho c^2$, where the mass density is ρ (observationally ρ seems to satisfy, $\rho > 10^{-31}$ g/cm³).

Again assuming negligible pressure, the energy density times a measure of the volume of the universe is constant. Hence

$$\rho a^3 = \rho_0 a_0{}^3 = \text{const.} \tag{52}$$

Substituting these results in equation (51) yields

$$\left(\frac{\dot{a}}{a} + \frac{1}{2}\frac{\dot{\phi}}{\phi}\right)^2 + \frac{\lambda}{a^2} = \frac{1}{4}(1 + \frac{2}{3}\omega)\left(\frac{\dot{\phi}}{\phi}\right)^2 + \frac{8\pi}{3\phi}\rho_0\left(\frac{a}{a}\right)^3. \tag{53}$$

Here ρ_0 and a_0 refer to values at some arbitrary fixed time t_0. In similar fashion equation (13) becomes

$$(d/dt)(\phi a^3) = [8\pi/(3 + 2\omega)]\rho_0 a_0^3. \tag{54}$$

After integration, equation (54) becomes

$$\phi a^3 = [8\pi/(3 + 2\omega)]\rho_0 a_0^3(t - t_c). \tag{55}$$

The constant of integration, t_c in equation (55), can be evaluated by considerations of Mach's principle.

As before, we introduce Mach's principle into this problem by expressing $\phi(t)$ as an advanced-wave integral over all matter. Equations (46) and (47) require some assumption about the history of matter in the universe. We assume that the universe expands from a highly condensed state. It is possible that in the intense gravitational field of this condensed state, matter is created. For a closed universe, matter from a previous cycle may be regenerated in this high-temperature state. In view of our present state of ignorance, there seems to be little point in speculating about the processes involved. In any case the creation process lies outside the present theory.

We assume, therefore, an initial state at the beginning of the expansion ($t = 0$) with $a \cong 0$ and matter already present. Although pressure would certainly be important in such a highly condensed state, with expansion the pressure would rapidly fall and no great harm is done to the model if pressure effects are neglected. In fact, an integration of the initial high-pressure phase for a particular cosmological model shows explicitly that it may be neglected to good approximation.

It is assumed that the inertial reaction, and hence ϕ, at time t_c is determined uniquely by the matter distribution from $t = 0$ to $t = t_0$. Hence, if equation (46) is integrated over all 3-space from $t = 0$ to $t_1 > t_0$, the surface integral obtained from the left-hand side should vanish. Initial conditions for equations (53) and (55) in the form of values of a and ϕ at $t = 0$ and a value of the constant t_c must be so chosen that the surface integral from equation (46) vanishes. In order for this surface integral to be meaningful at $t = 0$, the a must be at least infinitesimally positive on the surface, otherwise the metric tensor is singular. If $t_c = 0$ and $\phi = 0$ on this surface, the surface integral vanishes. This follows because the vanishing factors ϕ and $a^3\phi_{,0}$ [see equation (55)] occur in the integral. It is concluded, therefore, that the appropriate initial conditions are $a = \phi = 0$ with $t_c = 0$. It should be noted that the other surface integral, over the surface $t = t_c$, vanishes since η and all its gradients are zero on this surface (advanced-wave solution).

Letting $t_c = 0$ in equation (55) and combining with equation (53) gives

$$[(\dot{a}/a) + \frac{1}{2}(\dot{\phi}/\phi)]^2 + \lambda a^{-2} = \frac{1}{4}(1 + \frac{2}{3}\omega)(\dot{\phi}/\phi)^2 + (1 + \frac{2}{3}\omega)(\dot{\phi}/\phi)(1/t), \tag{57}$$

$$\phi a^3 = [8\pi/(3 + 2\omega)]\rho_0 a_0^3 t. \tag{58}$$

It can be seen that for sufficiently small time the term $1/a^2$ in equation (57) is negligible and the solution differs only infinitesimally from the flat-space case.

The resulting equations can be integrated exactly with the initial conditions

$$\phi = a = 0; \qquad t = 0. \tag{59}$$

As both equations (57 and (58) are now (in this approximation) homogeneous in (a, a_0), the solution is determined within a scale factor in a only.

This solution, good for the early expansion phases (i.e., $a \gg t$), is

$$\phi = \phi_0(t/t_0)^r,$$
$$a = a_0(t/t_0)^q, \tag{60}$$

with

$$r = 2/(4 + 3\omega), \tag{61}$$

$$q = (2 + 2\omega)/(4 + 3\omega), \tag{62}$$

and

$$\phi_0 = 8\pi[(4 + 3\omega)/2(3 + 2\omega)]\rho_0 t_0^2. \tag{63}$$

For the flat-space case, the solution is exact for all $t > 0$.

It should be noted that equation (63) is compatible with equation (1), for in equation (1) M is of the order of magnitude of $\rho_0 c^3 t_0^3$ and R is approximately ct_0. Thus, the initial conditions are compatible with Mach's principle as it has been formulated here.

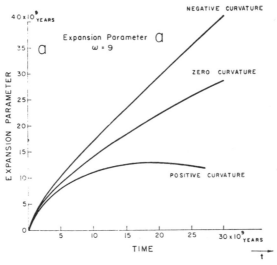

Fig. 1. The expansion parameter a as a function of t for the three cases, closed, open, and flat space with $\omega = 9$.

For a nonflat space, the only feasible method of integrating equations (57) and (58) beyond the range of validity of the above solution is numerical integration. An example of an integration is plotted in Figs. 1 and 2, where a and ϕ are plotted as a function of time for the three cases of positive, zero, and negative curvature with $\omega = 9$.

It should be noted that for $\omega \geq 6$, and the flat-space solution, the time dependence of a differs only slightly from the corresponding case in general relativity (Einstein–deSitter) where $a \sim t^{2/3}$. Consequently, it would be difficult to distinguish between the two theories on the basis of space geometry only. In similar fashion the mass density required for a particular Hubble age $a/\dot{a}$ (flat space) is the same as for general relativity if $\omega \gg 1$. For $\omega = 6$ there is only a 2 per cent difference between the two theories.

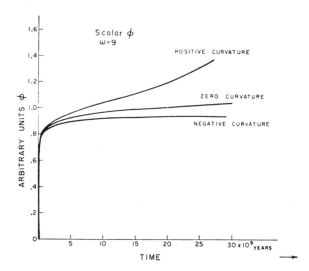

Fig. 2. The scalar ϕ, in arbitrary units, as a function of t for the three cases, closed, open, and flat space, with $\omega = 9$.

On the other hand, stellar evolutionary rates are a sensitive function of the gravitational constant, and this makes an observational test of the theory possible. This matter is discussed in a companion article by one of us (R. H. D.).[25]

At the beginning of this article a problem was posed, to understand within the framework of Mach's principle the lawys of physics seen within a laboratory set rotating within a universe otherwise almost empty. We are now in a position to begin to understand this problem. Consider a laboratory, idealized to a spherical mass shell with a mass m and radius r, and stationary in the comoving coordinate system given by equations (50) with equations (60), (61), (62), and (63) satisfied. Imagine now that the laboratory is set rotating about an axis with an angular velocity α_0. This rotation affects the metric tensor inside the spherical shell in such a way as to cause the gyroscope to precess with an angular velocity[5] [also see equation (27)]

$$\alpha = (8m/3rc^2\phi_0)\alpha_0, \tag{64}$$

where ϕ_0 is given by equation (63). Equation (64) is valid in the weak-field approximation only for which $m/(rc^2\phi_0) \ll 1$. Substituting equation (63) in equation (64) gives

$$\alpha = [2(3 + 2\omega)/3\pi(4 + 3\omega)] \cdot (m/rc^2\rho_0 t_0^2)\alpha_0. \tag{65}$$

It may be noted that if the matter density ρ_0 of the universe is decreased, with t_0 const, α increases. Thus, as the universe is emptied, the Thirring–Lense precession of the gyroscope approaches more closely the rotation velcotity α_0 of the laboratory. Unfortunately, the weak-field approximation does not permit a study of the limiting process $\rho_0 \to 0$.

In another publication by one of us (C. B.) other aspects of the theory, including conservation laws, will be discussed.

Acknowledgments

The authors wish to acknowledge helpful conversations with C. Misner on various aspects of this problem, and one of us (C. B.) is indebted for advice on this and other matters in his thesis. The authors wish also to thank P. Roll and D. Curott for the machine integration of the cosmological solutions [equations (49 and 50)], a small part of which is plotted in Figs. 1 and 2.

Appendix

In general relativity the equation of motion of a point particle, without spin, moving in a gravitational field only, may be obtained from the variational principle

$$0 = \delta \int m(g_{ij}u^i u^j)^{1/2} ds, \tag{66}$$

or

$$(d/ds)(mn_i) - \tfrac{1}{2}mg_{jk,i}u^j u^k = 0. \tag{67}$$

If the mass in equation (66) is assumed to be a function of position,

$$m = m_0 f(x), \tag{68}$$

an added force term appears and

$$(d/ds)(mu_i) - \tfrac{1}{2}mg_{jk,i}u^j u^k - m_{,i} = 0. \tag{69}$$

Both equations are consistent with the constraint condition $u^i u_i = 1$. It should be noted that because of the added force term in equation (69), the particle does not move on a goedesic of the geometry.

If now the geometry is redefined in such a way that the new metric tensor is (conformal transformation)

$$\bar{g}_{ij} = f^2 g_{ij}, \tag{70}$$

and

$$d\bar{s}^2 = f^2 ds^2, \qquad \bar{u}^i = f^{-1}u^i.$$

Equation (69) may be written as

$$(d/d\bar{s})\,(m_0\bar{u}_i) \,-\, \tfrac{1}{2}m_0\bar{g}_{jk,i}\bar{u}^j\bar{u}^k = 0. \tag{71}$$

The particle moves on a geodesic of the new geometry. With the new units of length, time, and mass appropriate for this new geometry, the mass of the particle is m_0, a constant.

Notes and References to Appendix 7

[1] E. T. Whittaker, *History of the Theories of Aether and Electricity* (Thomas Nelson and Sons, New York, 1951).

[2] I. Newton, *Principia Mathematica Philosophiae Naturalis* (1686) (reprinted by University of California Press, Berkeley, California, 1934).

[3] G. Berkeley, *The Principles of Human Knowledge*, paragraphs 111–117, 1710-*De Motu* (1726).

[4] E. Mach, *Conservation of Energy*, note No. 1, 1872 (reprinted by Open Court Publishing Company, LaSalle, Illinois, 1911), and *The Science of Mechanics*, 1883 (reprinted by Open Court Publishing Company, LaSalle, Illinois, 1902), Chap. II, Sec. VI.

[5] Because of the Thirring–Lense effect [H. Thirring and J. Lense, *Phys. Zeits.* **19**, 156 (1918)], the rotating laboratory would have a weak effect on the axis of the gyroscope.

[6] A. Komar, Ph.D. thesis, Princeton University, 1956 (unpublished).

[7] D. W. Sciama, *Monthly Notices Roy. Astron Soc.* **113**, 34 (1953); *The Unity of the Universe* (Doubleday & Company, Inc., New York, 1959), Chaps. 7–9.

[8] R. H. Dicke, *Am. Scientist*, **47**, 25 (1959).

[9] R. H. Dicke, *Science*, **129**, 621 (1959).

[10] R. H. Dicke, *Am. J. Phys.*, **29**, 344 (1960).

[11] P. A. M. Dirac, *Proc. Roy. Soc.* (*London*), **A165**, 199 (1938).

[12] E. P. Wigner has questioned the physical significance of Riemannian geometry on other grounds [Relativity Seminar, Stevens Institute, May 9, 1961 (unpublished)].

[13] B. Hoffman, *Phys. Rev.* **89**, 49 (1953).

[14] R. Eötvös, *Ann. Physik*, **68**, 11 (1922).

[15] V. W. Hughes, H. G. Robinson, and V. Beltran–Lopez, *Phys. Rev. Letters*, **4**, 342 (1960).

[16] P. Jordon, *Schwerkraft and Weltall* (Friedrich Vieweg and Sohn, Braunschweig, 1955); *Z. Physik*, **157**, 112 (1959). In this second reference, Jordan has taken cognizance of the objections of Fierz (see reference 19) and has written his variational principle in a form which differs in only two respects from that expressed in Equation (16). See also reference 20.

[17] For a discussion of this, see H. Bondi, *Cosmology*, 2nd edition, 1960.

[18] L. Landau and E. Liftschitz, *Classical Theory of Fields* (Addison–Wesley Publishing Company, Reading, Massachusetts, 1951).

[19] M. Fierz, *Helv. Phys. Acta.*, **29**, 128 (1956).

[20] There are but two formal differences between the field equations of this theory and those of the particular form of Jordan's theory given in *Z. Physik*, **157**, 112 (1959). First, Jordan has defined his scalar field variable reciprocal to ϕ. Thus, the simple wave character of the scalar field equation (equation (13)) is not so clear and the physical arguments based on Mach's principle and leading to equation (4) have not been satisfied. Second, as a result of its outgrowth from his five-dimensional theory, Jordan has limited his matter variables to those of the electromagnetic field.

[21] C. Misner and P. Putnam, *Phys. Rev.*, **116**, 1045 (1959).

[22] This form of solution was suggested to one of us (C. B.) by C. Misner.

[23] G. M. Clemence, *Revs. Modern Phys.*, **19**, 361 (1947).

[24] G. M. Clemence (private communication). One of us (R. H. D.) is grateful for helpful correspondence and conversations with Dr. Clemence on this and other aspects of celestial mechanics.

[25] R. H. Dicke, *Revs. Modern Phys.*, (to be published) (see appendix 10).

Appendix 8

Lee–Yang Vector Field and Isotropy of the Universe*

R. H. Dicke

Reprinted from *The Physical Review*, Vol. 126, No. 4, 1580–1581, May 15, 1962

Lee and Yang suggested that, associated with heavy-particle conservation, there may exist an analog of the electromagnetic field, a field for which nucleons and antinucleons would serve as positive and negative "charges." It is shown that the null result from a recent repetition of the Eötvös experiment implies that, if it exists, the Lee–Yang interaction is at most only 10^{-7} of the gravitational interaction. This great weakness does not imply that the field does not exist. However, with the assumption of the isotropy of the average matter distribution of the universe, the Lee–Yang antisymmetric field tensor vanishes when averaged over sufficiently large volumes. This implies that, if the Lee–Yang field exists, nucleons and antinucleons are present in equal numbers in the universe presumably gathered in matter and antimatter galaxies. However, it is found that the fact that a copious stream of γ rays is not present in the cosmic rays can be used to exclude such numbers of antimatter galaxies. It is concluded that the Lee–Yang field probably does not exist.

Connected with baryon conservation, Lee and Yang[1] have suggested that there may exist a neutral, massless, gauge-invariant vector field analogous to the electromagnetic field. Nucleons and antinucleons would serve as positive and negative "charges," the sources of this field, and in motion constitute "currents." The tremendous circulating nucleons currents in the galaxy could result in the generation of the Lee–Yang analog of the magnetic field. The Lee–Yang analog of the electric field would lead to a repulsion between matter, tending to reduce the gravitational acceleration. It is evident that if it exists, the Lee–Yang interaction is weak, or matter would fall up not down.

As shown by Lee and Yang, the null result of the Eötvös experiment[2] imposes a severe restriction upon the strength of the Lee–Yang field. The Eötvös experiment demonstrated with an accuracy of about 5 parts in 10^9 that gravitational accelerations are independent of the atomic weight of the falling body. More recently[3] it has been shown that the accelerations toward the sun of copper and lead are equal to an accuracy of one part in 10^{10}.

Consider the force exerted on an atom by the sun through the Lee–Yang analog of an electric field. This force is proportional to A, the nucleon number of the atom, and is independent of the motions of the nucleons inside the nucleus. Hence, the Lee–Yang force is independent of the binding energy of the nucleus, but this implies that the resulting acceleration of the atom depends upon the mass (and binding energy).

It is easily shown that the fractional difference in acceleration, toward the sun, of two different substances of different atomic weight is

$$\frac{\delta g}{g} \cong \gamma \left\langle \frac{A}{M} \right\rangle_s \left[\left(\frac{A}{M} \right)_2 - \left(\frac{A}{M} \right)_1 \right], \tag{1}$$

* This work was supported in part by research contracts with the Office of Naval Research and the U. S. Atomic Energy Commission.

where A/M is the ratio of the nucleon number to atomic weight, $(A/M)_i$ referring to the appropriate average over the sun. γ is the strength of the Lee–Yang interaction, relative to gravitation. Assuming that for copper and lead

$$|\delta g/g| < 10^{-10}, \tag{2}$$

and inserting the values

$$\langle A/M \rangle_s \sim 1, \qquad (A/M)_{Cu} = 0.9993, \qquad (AnM)_{Pb} = 1.003, \tag{3}$$

gives

$$\gamma < 10^{-7}. \tag{4}$$

Thus, the Lee–Yang interaction, if it exists, is at most only 10^{-7} of the strength of the gravitational interaction.

While it might be argued that the great weakness of the Lee–Yang interaction implies that it is nonexistent, this argument is believed to have little merit. It is interesting therefore that a symmetry argument, independent of the strength of the interaction, can be used to cast doubt upon the existence of this field.

Making the usual assumption of uniformity and isotropy of the universe, when averaged over sufficiently large volumes, it is possible to conclude that gauge-invariant vector fields in general, and the Lee–Yang field in particular, vanish when averaged over large volumes. This conclusion is based on a symmetry condition, is therefore independent of the strength of the coupling to the field, but is also valid only to the extent that the assumption of the isotropy of the universe is valid. It should be remembered that we see only a part of the universe, and that imperfectly. The assumption of uniformity and isotropy always involves an element of faith.

This symmetry argument is easily given. Expressed in co-moving coordinates (time orthogonal), matter is assumed to be, when averaged over large volumes, isotropically distributed about any space point. The average vector field, derived from this average matter distribution, must then exhibit this same symmetry. All components of any three-vector in this coordinate system must vanish, for there is no preferred direction in this space. In particular, electric and magnetic fields and all components of the analogous-antisymmetric Lee–Yang field tensor must vanish. Although, the symmetry argument is based upon the use of a particular coordinate system, its conclusion is generally valid, for the vanishing of all the components of a tensor in one coordinate system implies its vanishing in any coordinate system. Because of the "Maxwell equations" of the Lee–Yang field,

$$J^i = F^{ij}{}_{,j} = [1/(-g)^{1/2}][(-g)^{1/2}F^{ij}]_{,j}. \tag{5}$$

J^i the nucleon four-current, vanishes if $F^{ij} = 0$. This in turn implies that, taken over sufficiently large volumes, the nucleon number density of space is zero. Thus nucleons and antinucleons must be present in equal numbers.

The structure and history of the galaxy is such that it is inconceivable that nucleons and antinucleons should be present in comparable numbers in the same galaxy. It must be presumed that if the Lee–Yang field exists, and the symmetry argument is valid, the universe must be populated with both nucleon and antinucleon galaxies. Such a universe has been suggested previously.[4] It is difficult to see how such a separation of matter into nucleon and antinucleon galaxies could occur. Furthermore, a universe populated by a mixture of matter and antimatter galaxies, should contain many energetic photons, having their origin in the annihilation of a part of the gas masses of colliding galaxies. The expected collision rate is sufficiently great that, under these assumptions and contrary to what is observed,[5] a large γ-ray flux should appear in the cosmic radiation. The past annihilation of only one part in a million of the matter content of the universe would lead to an expected photon flux in the cosmic radiation of roughly $\frac{1}{3}$ of a photon per second per square centimeter, several orders of magnitude too great.

To summarize, one can conclude, on the basis of the symmetry argument, one of three things:

(1) The universe is populated with matter and anti-matter galaxies.

(2) The assumption of uniformity of the universe is invalid.

(3) The Lee–Yang vector field does not exist.

As the possibilities (1) and (2) seem unpromising, it seems very likely that the Lee–Yang field does not exist. It should be remarked that the above symmetry argument is without substance for the short-range vector field proposed recently by Schwinger[6] as a replacement for the Lee–Yang field.

Notes and References to Appendix 8

[1] T. D. Lee and C. N. Yang, *Phys. Rev.*, **98**, 1501 (1955).

[2] R. v. Eötvös, D. Pekar, and E. Fekete, *Ann. Phys.*, **68**, 11 (1922).

[3] R. H. Dicke, P. Roll, D. Currott, and R. Krotkov (to be published).

[4] P. Morrison, *Am. J. Phys.*, **26**, 358 (1958), and M. Goldhaber, *Science*, **124**, 218 (1956) have given discussions which are relevant.

[5] T. L. Cline, *Phys. Rev. Letters*, **7**, 109 (1961).

[6] J. Schwinger, *Phys. Rev.*, **125**, 397 (1962).

Appendix 9

The Earth and Cosmology

The earth may be affected by the distant matter of the universe through a long-range interaction.

R. H. Dicke*

Reprinted from *Science*, November 9, 1962, Vol. 138, No. 3541, pages 653–664

Is the earth affected by its cosmological setting in the universe? It is to be presumed that the solar system was molded at its birth by galactic conditions which in turn reflected the primordial chaos of the primitive galaxy. However, we are not concerned here with questions of this type, interesting though they are, but rather with a problem of even grander proportions: Is there an effect upon the earth, here and now, of the distribution of matter in the universe? As the universe expands, as distant matter moves away from us, are there effects upon the earth of this changing distribution of matter?

* The author is Cyrus Fogg Brackett professor of physics, Palmer Physical Laboratory, Princeton University, Princeton, N.J.

This problem is a complicated one and can be approached from three ortho-gonal directions, from the viewpoints of astrophysicists, geophysicists, and physicists.

The traditional answer of the physicists is clear and unambiguous: "Distant matter of the universe, spherically distributed about the earth, is without a notice-able effect on the solar system. There are no locally induced consequences of the expansion of the universe."

A small minority of physicists, of which I happen to be one, have taken the contrary view, believing that this principle of independence is not established. P. A. M. Dirac[1] noting certain coincidences between dimensionless astrophysical constants and the dimensionless gravitational coupling constant, suggested a possible causal connection between the physical "constant" and the structure of the universe.

P. Jordan[2] and his students and assoiates[3] carried out an extensive theoret-ical development aimed at establishing a proper formal structure for Dirac's ideas. More recently my students and I have been concerned with the problem as it relates to Mach's principle.[4]

Astrophysical and geophysical implications of the question have been dis-cussed previously by P. Jordan[2,5] and by me.[6,7] Certain aspects of the problem, as it relates to geophysics, are discussed in greater detail here. First, however, I present the question from the viewpoint of the physicist.

Physical Framework

While knowledge of significance to cosmology that is directly based upon ex-periment and observation is meager, the confidence of the physicist in the appli-cability and correctness of the basic tenets of relativity theory is considerable. This all-powerful theoretical tool imposes constraints so severe that relatively few cosmological theories in accord with these principles can be devised. It should be emphasized that although there are few significant direct observations on gravitation and cosmology, the host of high-energy experiments performed in the laboratory, interpretation of which requires the use of relativity, serve to establish the correct-ness of the basic relativistic foundations of physics and consequently, in a sense, represent indirect support of gravitational theory. This phalanx of observational evidence strengthens the hand of the physicist who must deal with a strange and dark physical situation.

It is paradoxical that the relativity principle, this strong instrument which can be applied to the cosmological problem, actually had its origin in cosmology. When the British philosopher Bishop Berkeley[8] objected to Newton's concept of an absolute physical space[9], his objections were based on the impossibility of observing position or motion with respect to such an empty space. He emphasized that what is observed is position and motion of matter *relative* to other matter. He, and later Mach, emphasized that inertial effects should be associated with accelera-tion of matter relative to other matter, not relative to an absolute space.

Out of Mach's principle (perhaps better called Berkeley's principle) there eventually sprang the package of ideas which we call relativity. Actually, historically it took a number of laboratory experiments, by Michelson and Morley, Kennedy and Thorndike, Trouton and Noble, and others, to initiate the development of these ideas, and the classic ideas of Berkeley did not play a direct role. However, we can now see how these fundamental relativistic principles are rooted in Berkeley's philosophy and in a number of fundamental observations and experiments, of which the modern ones by Hughes and his associates and by Drever, the Eötvös experiment as recently repeated by the Princeton group, the long series of elementary-particle experiments at high energies, and the observed perihelion rotation of the planet Mercury constitute the chief bases.

This, however, is not the sole heritage from Berkeley's philosophy. We have also the direct cosmological implication that the inertial stage upon which local physical phenomena occur is determined by, and anchored to, the distant matter of the universe. This means, not that distant stars serve as beacon lights to tell us where an absolute physical space lies, but rather that the distant matter in the universe is in some direct and prosaic way a source of the inertial properties of space. Thus, from Berkeley's point of view, inertial forces may be considered as interactions with distant matter in the universe.

The only relativistic means available to us for producing quasi-static interactions between bodies, widely separated, are the long-range fields. The prototype of such fields is electromagnetism. The electrostatic interactions between widely separated charged bodies is well known: so is the fact that electromagnetic waves exist, propagating with the velocity of light, and the fact that, associated with the waves, through quantum fluctuation effects, there are particles, the photons, having zero rest mass and a spin angular momentum of $\hbar$, where $\hbar = \frac{1}{2}\pi$ (Planck's constant).

The principles of relativity and quantum mechanics provide us with a rigid classification for long-range fields. All such fields may be divided into two classes, boson and fermion, characterized respectively by particles with integral and half integral multiples of $\hbar$ for spin angular momentum. The necessity for interchanging pairs of ferminos makes it unlikely that interesting and detectable long-range, quasi-static interactions will occur through a fermion field.

When we limit ourselves to boson fields there is a further classification provided by relativity. All such fields may be classified as scalar, vector, tensor, and higher-rank tensor. On the assumption that nature, although perhaps capricious, is not malicious, we shall assume that higher-rank tensors will not occur. The tensor field already provides such exquisitely beautiful mathematical difficulties that higher-rank tensors should be prohibited by fiat.

This classification, provided for us by the tensor calculus, is in itself a direct heritage from the ideas of Berkeley. If, as suggested by Berkeley, it is only the position of matter relative to other matter that is significant, an absolute coordinate system in space should be without significance. If all coordinate systems (including time as a fourth coordinate) are of equal validity, the mathematical tool appropriate for treating physical problems, including geometry, is the tensor calculus, for it is designed to treat geometry analytically but without reference to a specific coordinate system. In the tensor calculus a scalar is a field variable for which a single parameter is a function of position (and time). For a vector field, in a four-dimensional space, there are four position-dependent parameters, and for a general tensor field, 16.

A long-range vector field is known. It is that associated with electromagnetism. The four field quantities are the electromagnetic potentials. It can be shown that the requirements of relativity plus the assumption of charge conservation are sufficient to establish the essential features of the theory of electromagnetism.

A gauge-invariant vector theory, electromagnetism, or some similar vector field generated by a strongly conserved "charge" cannot play an important role, in the sense of introducing a quasi-static interaction, in the cosmology of a uniform isotropic universe. The reason for this is that, being vectors mirroring the symmetry of space, the electric and magnetic fields must average to zero over large volumes in a space which is isotropic (in large-volume averages). Thus, such vector fields are not a suitable source of long-range influence of distant matter on the laboratory.

Similarly, a long-range symmetric tensor field is believed to exist in the form of the gravitational field. This, Einstein's theory of gravitation, satisfies general relativistic requirements with the additional assumption of the equivalence principle. Thus, it too involves many experiments which, at first glance, seem to have nothing to do with gravitation.

It is in connection with the tensor field that a direct relation between inertial forces and the distribution of distant matter appears, a formal basis for some of the ideas of Berkeley and Mach thus being established. It is found that the interaction of a tensor field with a particle leads to two different types of forces. One is a force proportional to the acceleration. We recognize it as the inertial force. The other type of force is quadratic in the four-velocity of the particle (a vector) and is recognized as a gravitational force. Both types of forces may be called gravitational. Both are derived from the same term of an action principle, and a particle can be said to move in such a way as always to balance inertial forces against other applied forces. The arbitrariness in the choice of coordinate system is mirrored in a similar arbitrariness in the force balance sheet. Through the use of coordinate transformations, inertial forces may be converted into gravitational forces, of opposite sign, as readily and arbitrarily as a clever book-keeper can transfer funds from the liability to the asset side of a ledger.

Another heritage from Berkeley, Mach, and Einstein is the idea that gravitational and inertial forces are universal, applying in the same way to all matter. If the inertial and gravitational forces acting upon a particle are to be associated with the whole-mass distribution about the particle, the motion of the particle is determined by the mass distribution and should be substantially independent of the type of particle. Thus, the tensor field would be expected to interact in the same way with all matter.

It is a property of a universal tensor force field of this type that it affects matter in bulk, modifying the lengths of meter sticks and the rates of clocks. It is usually most convenient to define the meter sticks and clocks as unmodified and to ascribe the effects of these variations to a non-Euclidian geometry of space. From this point of view—the traditional and most convenient one—the symmetric tensor is the metric tensor of a Riemannian geometry, and gravitational effects are elevated from the mundane forces of the physicist to the ethereal geometry of the mathematician. It should be recognized that this interpretation of the role of the tensor interaction is convenient but not essential.

While this metric tensor field carries information about the matter distribution of the universe, it apparently is incapable of expressing completely the whole of Mach's principle. This can be seen by noting that, in a universe empty except for a localized mass distribution, it is possible to journey off, leaving the matter far behind. The geometry becomes flat, and the resulting metric tensor ascribes inertial properties to space, with no matter about. Further-more, the space interior to a spherical mass distribution is flat, and nothing about the geometry of the space reflects either the total mass or the radius of this distribution. Thus, as noted earlier, it is usually believed that the spherically distributed distant matter is without effect on the solar system (except for the determination of inertial coordinate systems).

Only one more possible type of long-range field remains to be considered, the scalar. If there is any truth in the proposition that nature is simple, this field should exist and play an important role, for it is the simplest of the three massless, boson fields. Strangely enough, this primitive field is generally believed not to exist.

It is one of those strange twists, so queer that we almost miss it, that here is a field whose properties are much more certain than its existence. While the basic properties of a long-range scalar interaction are known to few physicists, they follow in such a direct way from general relativistic requirements that one can have considerable confidence in their correctness.

The scalar field is believed to be nonexistent because of the lack of a clear indication in laboratory experiments of effects due to its presence. However, I have shown[10] that this type of interaction must be very weak, of the same general strength as gravitation, and furthermore that the force masquerades as gravitation, being so similar to gravitation in its effects that it could be distinguished only with great difficulty. Five percent of the force we call gravitation could be due to the scalar field (the remainder being true gravitation associated with the tensor field) and we would have no way of knowing it.

Of course, the fact that a field is almost undetectable in the laboratory is not a sufficient reason for suspecting that it exists. On the contrary, there is every reason for divesting physics of useless encumbrances, of which an unobserved field would be a prime example. However, viewed in the larger arena of the cosmologist with the broad vista of the whole universe stretched before him, this scalar field, and the question of its existence, is of prime importance, for this is the only one of the three fields by means of which the matter distribution of the universe can affect the solar system and laboratory physics, apart from the trivial determination, by distant matter, of the orientation of inertial coordinate axes associated with the tensor field. The fact is that, if the scalar field exists and is correctly described by applying the standardized relativistic rituals, this scalar field provides a direct link between locally observed physical laws and the matter distribution of the universe. Furthermore, a particular form of scalar interaction serves to eliminate several deficiencies in general relativity theory with respect to Mach's principle and to bring the theory more nearly in accord with Mach's principle. Also, as is explained below, if the scalar field exists, it becomes possible to understand why the gravitational interaction is so weak.

The properties of the long-range scalar interaction have been derived from general relativistic principles elsewhere. Here I merely summarize the chief results.

(1) While the quantum fluctuation effects are presumably not of importance for cosmology, I summarize them for completeness: There is associated with the scalar field an uncharged, spindless particle. It has zero rest mass, hence travels always with the velocity of light.

(2) Treated as a classical field, the scalar interaction causes an attraction between bits of matter. As in the case of gravitation, this force falls off inversely as the square of the distance.

(3) It has been shown[10] that the interaction, if it exists, would be expected to have a strength roughly within an order of magnitude of that of the gravitational interaction. The reason for this is the large contribution to the value of the scalar interaction of the enormous amounts of matter at great distance in the universe. In comparison, the contribution from some local body, such as the sun, is minuscule, and this leads to a weak interaction. One cannot obtain a strong interaction by introducing a strong coupling to matter because both contributions to the value of the scalar (from nearby and from distant matter) increase together

(4) One fundamental property of the scalar field, known to very few physicists, is that the mass of a particle interacting with a scalar field is a function of the scalar. This is such a fundamental property of the interaction that I attempt to find some simple way to illustrate its necessity. Let us consider a static scalar field acting on a particle. The force exerted is given by the gradient of the scalar φ. This force is equal to the rate of change with respect to proper time τ of momentum of the particle:

$$\frac{d}{d\tau} P_x = -\frac{\partial \varphi}{\partial x} \tag{1}$$

This implies an acceleration of the particle in the X direction. On the other hand, the fourth component of the particle momentum is its energy, and we have:

$$\frac{d}{d\tau} P_4 = \frac{d}{d\tau} E = -\frac{\partial \varphi}{\partial t} = 0 \tag{2}$$

since the scalar field is static. But this implies that the particle's energy is constant even though the particle is accelerating. This is possible if the particle loses rest energy mc^2 as it gains kinetic energy. A closer examination shows that the rest mass must be a linear function of φ if the particle is to interact with this scalar field. More generally, for any scalar field λ, the mass of an interacting particle must be a function of the scalar.

(5) The functional form of the mass dependence must be substantially the same for all elementary properties. This is not a relativistic requirement but depends for its validity upon the great precision of the Eötvös experiment, which shows that all types of matter are accelerated gravitationally in the same way.

(6) Because of this mass dependence, the magnitude of the scalar is in principle measurable by determining the ratio of the mass of some elementary particle, such as the proton, to the characteristic gravitational mass $(\hbar c/G)^{1/2}$. This ratio would vary if the scalar field variable at the location of the particle varied. This dimensionless ratio is roughly of the order of magnitude of

$$(Gm_p{}^2/\hbar c)^{1/2} \simeq 10^{-20} \tag{3}$$

(G is the gravitational constant and m_p is the mass of a proton). The anomalously small value can be understood as the effect of the enormous amounts of matter in distant parts of the universe generating a large scalar field and a mass dependence of the form

$$m = m_0 \, \lambda^{-1/2} \tag{4}$$

with λ a dimensionless scalar field variable and m_0 constant.[11]

(7) The scalar field does not interact with light rays or with other particles moving with the velocity of light. Thus, the gravitational deflection of light should be slightly less than the value expected from the gravitational weight of an object if a small part of the weight is due to the scalar interaction. In similar fashion the relativistic rotation rate of the perihelion of Mercury's orbit would be slightly less.

(8) The scalar field satisfies a wave equation with the contracted energy-momentum tensor of matter serving as the source of the scalar field. For a slowly moving astronomical body, an integral of the contracted energy-momentum tensor over the body gives the total energy or mass of the body. Thus, for those cases where gravitational fields are detected and measured, the source of the scalar field is, as is the source of gravitation, the mass of the body.

(9) When the masses of the elementary particles comprising a meter stick vary, the meter stick changes its length, the length being proportional inversely to the masses of the elementary particles. These length changes are in principle measurable, for they can be determined by making comparisons with the invariant length $(G\hbar/c^3)^{1/2} \simeq 10^{-33}$ centimeter. In similar fashion the rate of an atomic clock is proportional to the mass of its elementary particles.

(10) For practical reasons the use of the invariant units of mass, length, and time given by the quantities $(\hbar c/G)^{1/2}$, $(G\hbar/c^3)^{1/2}$, and $(G\hbar/c^5)^{1/2}$ is inconvenient. If, instead, we prefer to use units of measure based on the particle, such as m, $\hbar/mc$, and $\hbar/mc^2$, this can be brought about by fiat, a transformation of units being introduced which results in particle mass being constant by definition. It is found that such a transformation of units leads to a dependence of the locally measured gravitational "constant" upon the field scalar, particle masses now being constant. It is obvious that, measured with these new units, the spatial geometry is now different. The metric tensor of the new geometry is conformably related to the old metric tensor. It should be noted that the gravitational coupling constant

$$(Gm^2/\hbar c) \simeq 10^{-40} \tag{5}$$

was originally interpreted as variable, as a result of the scalar dependence of $m = m_0 \lambda^{-1/2}$, the mass of an elementary particle. Expressed in new units of measure, this coupling constant varies because G varies, being $G = G_0 \lambda^{-1}$, with G_0 a constant.

(11) To preserve, formally, the validity of Einstein's general relativity theory, the scalar field was introduced above as an ordinary "matter field", Einstein's field equation for the metric tensor being satisfied. However, after the transformation of units, which results in the gravitational constant being variable, the scalar field loses its character as a "matter field" and becomes incorporated into the gravitational field, which may now be described as scalar plus tensor. In this form of the theory, the gravitational field equations were first given and discussed by Jordan[2] and his co-workers and later, in connection with Mach's principle, were discussed by Brans and me.[4]

Cosmology and the Scalar Field

What, then, is the cosmological setting of the earth? The earth is surrounded by an essentially spherical distribution of galaxies. While departures from uniformity in the distribution of matter are great, the distribution is believed to be sufficiently uniform in large-volume averages to support the somewhat idealized picture of the isotropic universe.

This universe is observed to be expanding uniformly with a reciprocal fractional expansion rate (or Hubble age) of slightly over 10^{10} years. Again, in the expansion there are departures from uniformity in the velocities of the galaxies of about 200 to 300 kilometers per second.

We have seen that as a means by which the distribution of distant matter can influence the earth, only three fields merit serious attention—the scalar, the vector, and the tensor fields. Let us consider first the tensor field of gravitation. As was mentioned previously, its local influence, having an origin in distant matter, seems to be limited to the association of local inertial coordinate axes with the distribution of distant matter. It appears to be quite precisely true that a local gyroscopic axis, such as the perpendicular to the invariant plane of the planetary orbits, continues to point at a fixed point with respect to the distribution of distant galaxies.

It might be thought that there could be more than one tensor field, and that consequently there could be additional effects of distant matter. However, it has been shown, through the very precise experiment of Hughes and Drever, that the existence of more than one tensor field is unlikely.[12]

It was argued earlier that a gauge-invariant vector field, such as electromagnetism, could not be important for cosmology because of the isotropy of the universe.

The most interesting interaction, from the viewpoint of the cosmologist, is that induced by the scalar field, for if this field exists, the steady expansion of the universe should lead to interesting effects, locally observable. The reasons for this have already been given.

Briefly stated, the expansion of the universe results in a time variation of the basic part of the scalar, that contributed by distant matter. As has been discussed, this variable scalar can be considered to affect the masses of elementary particles, or alternatively, with the proper choice of units, the gravitational constant. In many ways this last interpretation is most convenient.

The choice of scalar which appears to be particularly significant for cosmology and Mach's principle is that given by Brans and me.[4] With this theory, the gravitational constant is generated as the reciprocal of the scalar. The theory is such that, with the scalar satisfying outgoing wave boundary conditions, the time rate of change of the scalar λ is given by

$$\dot{\lambda} = - G_0 \dot{G}/G^2 = 8\pi G_0 \rho t/(2\omega + 3) \tag{6}$$

where ρ and t are the matter density and age of the universe, respectively, and ω is a dimensionless parameter, probably about equal to 6.

There are three types of geometry possible, for a uniform isotropic universe. These are closed, flat, and hyperbolic spaces. For a flat space, and the matter in the form of galaxies, the Hubble age of the universe is

$$T_h = [(4 + 3\omega)/(2 + 2\omega)]t \simeq (3/2)t \tag{7}$$

The fractional time rate of change of the gravitational constant is

$$-(\dot{G}/G) = 2/(3\omega + 4)t \simeq 1/10t \tag{8}$$

Assuming that the Hubble age is 12×10^9 years one obtains 8×10^9 years for the age of the universe—a value in good agreement with a recent value[13] for the galactic age, 7.3×10^9 years, obtained from uranium decay. The resulting rate of decrease of the gravitational constant is 1 part in 10^{11} parts per year. With a closed universe this rate of decrease could be as great as 3 parts in 10^{11} per year. In Fig. 1, the reciprocal gravitational constant is given as a function of time for the best present choices of parameters.

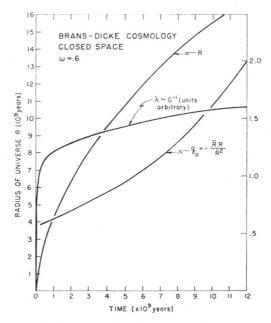

Fig. 1. A numerical integration by P. Roll and D. Curott of the cosmological equations of the Brans–Dicke theory for the case of a closed universe. R, The radius of the universe (in time units); q_0, the curvature parameter (for a flat space, $q_0 = 4/7$). The reciprocal of the gravitational constant is proportional to λ.

This, then, is the chief new element which a long-range scalar field would introduce into cosmology, a steadily weakening gravitational constant. The geophysical problem to be considered, then, is the following: If we assume that the gravitational constant has been steadily decreasing with time, what effect would such a decrease have had upon the earth throughout its history?

The scalar field, causing the gravitational constant to decrease now at a rate of perhaps 3 parts in 10^{11} per year and more rapidly in the past, would have important effects upon the earth. However, the earth is such a complex system that it would be difficult to use it as a source of evidence for or against the existence of the scalar field. It is better to assume tentatively that the field does exist and to attempt to unravel the complex implications of such a decrease. The validity of the analysis would then depend upon some future demonstration of the existence of the field.

The effects upon the earth of weakening gravitation would be widespread and diverse. Among the direct effects is the general expansion of the earth which must accompany a decrease in gravitational interaction (an increase in radius of 0.2 centimeter per century accompanying a rate of decrease of the gravitational constant of 3 parts in 10^{11} per year). The expansion is almost certain, if we accept the basic premise, but the mode of expansion is somewhat uncertain. Also it should be said that, if mantle convection occurs, the required general expansion is so modest that its effects would probably be lost in the much more noticeable display of the effects of convection.

The thermal history of the earth would require rethinking. A secular decrease in the internal pressure, as a result of weakening gravitation, would result in an adiabatic decrease in the internal temperature of the earth. However, the melting point of the deep mantle would be expected to decrease even more rapidly. While there is not enough known about the thermal properties of the earth's interior to raise speculation about its thermal history much above the level of conjecture, it is interesting to consider the problem of the flow of heat from the earth's core, and from the earth's surface, with a specific model, on the assumption that gravitation has been decreasing.

Another type of thermal problem concerns the surface temperature of the earth. The luminosity of the sun would be expected to vary approximately as G^8.[6,7] One would therefore conclude that the surface temperature of the earth had been higher in the past than it is now.[14]

The Earth's Expansion

The effect upon the earth's radius of a change in G by an amount δG was determined by G. Hess[15] and C. Murphy,[16] from calculations on earth models, to be approximately

$$\delta r/r = -0.1(\delta G/G) \qquad (9)$$

This is a decrease of 3 parts in 10^{12} per year for a fractional decrease in G of 3 parts in 10^{11}.

As it is the density of the earth's interior that must decrease, not the density of its surface, this expansion may take place in one or both of two ways. Tension cracks may open, to be filled with intrusions from the interior, or extensive magmatic extrusions from volcanos and surface fission could cause the interior of the earth to leak out through the crust, to form a new surface. This leakage might be at the rate necessary to bring about the needed expansion.

If this second mechanism dominates, the total lava flow from all volcanos and fissures must, on the average, total 9 cubic kilometers per year. There is no good estimate of the rate of extrusion of lava on the ocean floor, but a total flow rate for the whole earth of 1 cubic kilometer per year has been suggested. Thus, the observed flow rate appears to be too small by an order of magnitude.

One way of estimating an upper limit for the average rate of extrusion is to assume that the total mass of the crust and water above the Mohorovičić discontinuity had its genesis in such extrusions. This total represents an average extrusion rate of 1.8 cubic kilometers per year, at a density of 3.3 grams per cubic centimeter. This is only one-fifth of what is needed.

The amount of material needed, in the form of magma intrusions, to fill tension cracks sufficiently to bring about the necessary expansion is much less. If we assume such cracks to be 10 kilometers deep, the amount of magma required is only 0.012 cubic kilometer per year.

On the ocean floor there is a global system of tension cracks which might be associated with a general expansion of the earth. However, what is needed is a sound reason for believing that they are associated with a gradual expansion of the earth. More probably they are caused by a slow convection of the earth's interior.

It is now well known, as a result of the work of the oceanographers, particularly of H. W. Menard of the Scripps Institution of Oceanography and of M. Ewing and his group, of the Lamont Geological Observatory, that there is a globe-girdling system of oceanic ridges of which the mid-Atlantic Ridge is a prime example. These ridges are characterized by large medial tension cracks running most of their length. Because of their global character, these could be cracks associated with a general expansion.

This mechanism for a general expansion was suggested some years ago by T. J. Wilson,[17] B. C. Heezen,[18] and me.[6] However, the suggestion that the principal distributions of land masses could be accounted for by a gross expansion of an originally much smaller earth was made by S. W. Carey[19] and L. Egyed.[20]

Carey pictures an earth that originally had a continental crust and only 40 percent of the present surface area. He visualizes the earth as having expanded to its present size during the past few hundred million years, the land masses having cracked apart, and the cracks having widened to form the ocean basins. This would account nicely for the presence of the mid-ocean ridges, but there are difficulties to which we shall come.

This picture of the formation of the continental land masses from the fragmentation of one or two supercontinents is actually much older; it goes back to the ideas of Richard Owen (1857), A. Wegener (1915), A. L. Du Toit (1937), and others. Wegener suggested that these continental fragments of an original "Pangaea" land moved to their present positions not as a result of the effects of an expanding earth but as "ships of sial floating upon a basaltic layer". The implied role of mariner was a bit too exotic for the American geologists, and these old ideas were largely ignored.

There is now a substantial body of knowledge which supports either or both of these ideas—the expanding earth and "continental drift". It was pointed out 47 years ago by Wegener that the continental margins of North and South America parallel those of Europe and Africa, giving the North and South Atlantic oceans an approximately constant width. This would not of itself suggest strongly that the Atlantic Ocean was formed as a gigantic rift valley. However, the fact that the Mid-Atlantic Ridge divides the Atlantic into an eastern and a western half by bisecting all arcs of constant latitude makes it likely that all three features are causally connected (see Figs. 2 and 3).

There are at least three possible explanations for this association.

(1) The earth expanded by opening the Atlantic Ocean.

(2) Convection of the interior of the young earth moved the crust about, producing, among other features, the Atlantic Ocean. Convection then ceased, leaving the continents in their present positions.

(3) Convection of the earth's mantle is still continuing. The Atlantic Ocean is young, being only a few hundred million years old.[21]

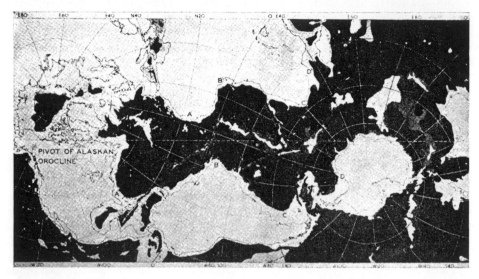

Fig. 2. The Atlantic Ocean, with the Mid-Atlantic Ridge dividing it down the middle.
[After S. W. Carey (19)].

Of these three explanations, the most reasonable at the moment appears to be the last. The Atlantic Ocean appears to be young. This is supported somewhat by the apparent correspondence of some of the stratigraphic sequences on the two sides of the Atlantic; by the scanty sedimentary deposits on the ocean bottom; by the presence of wide, young, tension cracks along the Mid-Atlantic Ridge; by the high heat flow from the ridge, suggesting a rising column in the mantle; by the seismic activity along the ridge; and particularly by the paleomagnetic data, which suggest a close proximity of the Americas and Europe-Africa a couple of hundred million years ago.

The expanding earth is also a possible explanation, accounting in a reasonable way for the growth of the Atlantic. The big problem here is the magnitude of the expansion that would have been required to form the Atlantic in 200 million years. The expansion rate needed is 300 times as great as that given by equation (9). It has been suggested that a relatively small change in G could bring about a phase change and lead to a large change in the radius of the earth. Such a large change in radius, occurring at a rate of 1 part in 10^9 parts per year, can probably be excluded by evidence concerning the earth's rotation for the past 2000 years, for such a change in radius would decrease the earth's rotation rate by 2 parts in 10^9 per year. The observations suggest an uncompensated increase of less than 1 part in 10^{10} parts per year.[22]

The problem posed by the Atlantic Ocean has been discussed in some detail. Actually there are many other features of the earth's surface which have a bearing on the problem of "continental drift" or "earth expansion," or both. Tension features such as the African rift valley, the Red Sea, and the Gulf of California are examples. The large lateral displacement along fault planes indicated by magnetic anomalies in the Pacific and the systems of island arcs and marginal trenches in the

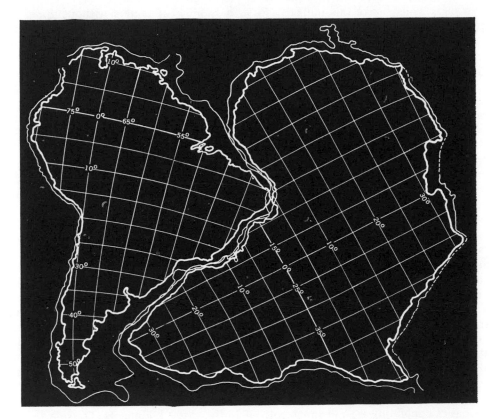

Fig. 3. The fit between the continental masses of Africa and South America. [After S. W. Carey (19)].

Pacific are indicative of the effects of mantle convection rather than of general expansion. Also, H. Hess[23] has suggested that the chains of guyots (discovered and investigated by him) are submerged islands which, with the atolls, mark old quiescent ridges which have subsided, suggesting convection rather than expansion.

While the evidence is not so strong as to present a clearly unambiguous story, the picture of an earth with a slowly convecting interior, gradually moving the continents, perhaps at a rate of 1 centimeter per year, is gradually unfolding.

The resulting gross changes in the earth's surface are so great as to mask almost completely any effects of a slow expansion of the earth.

Let us consider briefly the expansion hypothesis as it relates to the moon. Here the expansion in radius to be expected as a result of a change in G of 10 percent in 4×10^9 years is only 0.15 kilometer. Such an expansion would presumably have taken place by the extrusion of magma, which might well cover 20 per cent of the surface with basalt to a depth of 0.75 kilometer. It will be of interest to see some day if the maria are indeed basalt flows.

It has been suggested that the maria of the moon are seas of dust. There are two facts which make this unlikely. First, a number of craters without apparent cracks in the walls are filled inside and outside to the same level. Dust would not be expected to establish hydrostatic equilibrium under these conditions. Second, basins in the uplands are not filled with this "dust". Dust there probably is, but I would guess that it is only a thin layer.

It should be noted that there is no evidence of a "mantle convection" in the moon. Fault scraps are very rare on the moon, and there is no evidence of the large lateral displacements so common on the earth. Such a displacement of a fault plane cutting a crater would be very easily detected.

In summary, the evidence on the earth's surface favors "continental drift", with mantle convection as the driving mechanism. The miniscule effects of a modest expansion would be lost in the magnificent displays produced by convection. On the moon, however, the effects of a general expansion may be more readily apparent, for convection appears to be lacking. Expansion could lead to massive lava flows, perhaps in the form of fissure eruptions.

The problem posed by the effects of decreasing gravitation on the earth's interior, particularly in relation to heat flow, have been discussed by C. T. Murphy and me.[16] Here one is particularly hampered by lack of intimate knowledge of the earth's interior. Most of what we know is derived in an indirect, and often roundabout way from observations at the earth's surface. The strength of the earth's magnetic field and its variations with time, variations in the earth's potential, gravity anomalies, and heat-flow measurements all help describe the interior, but the best source of information has been seismic waves. These have told us about the basic structure of the interior, about density distribution and pressure, about the liquid core and the solid inner core. Unfortunately, we know little about the temperature distribution in the interior.

Deep in the earth's interior there is a liquid core, of radius 3500 kilometers, probably containing a solid inner core of radius 1400 kilometers. Outside this is the earth's mantle, extending to the crust, which is only 5 kilometers thick under the oceans and about 35 kilometers thick under the continents. The mantle appears to be essentially uniform in character, with only slow changes in density (and sound velocity), associated with changes in pressure, and temperature changes, as a function of depth.

Since the mantle of the earth is assumed to be essentially homogeneous chemically, a sample would be of the greatest importance, for two-thirds of the earth is mantle. It has been pointed out by H. Hess[24] that there are several fairly obvious places to look for bits of the mantle and that at these sites an interesting and rather uncommon rock appears.

A volcano seems to have its roots deep in the earth. In particular, the oceanic crust is so thin that a volcano here would be expected to derive its lava below the Mohorovičić discontinuity. The lava of these volcanos, like that of most continental volcanos, is composed of basalt, a material which may be presumed to be a low-melting-point component of the mantle. It might be expected that the lava would occasionally carry to the surface blocks of the raw, unmodified mantle itself. Foreign bodies (xenoliths) are found in volcanic lava, and one of these, peridotite, is the prime suspect in the search for the true mantle. This dense, dark, basic rock occurs in basaltic lavas from all over the world, from both continental and oceanic volcanos. Continental volcanos show other types of xenoliths as well, but this would be expected in view of the enormous thickness of crust to be penetrated.

From the discussion of the significance of the Mid-Atlantic Ridge and the rapid heat flow found there, if the general picture of mantle convection is correct, one would expect a predominance of basalt on the crest of the ridge, with the possibility of undifferentiated mantle protruding in places. It is notable, as Hess[24] pointed out, that St. Paul's Rock in the Atlantic is an enormous protrusion from the Mid-Atlantic Ridge of this same type of rock, essentially identical in composition, except for hydration, with samples yielded by volcanos from all over the world.

Finally, one would think that a steep escarpment on the ocean floor, where the crust is thin, might expose the mantle. This same type of rock has been dredged from the face of such an escarpment under the Atlantic. A hydrated form of this same rock, peridotite, has been found.

Peridotite is a relatively uncommon rock. Classified as igneous, it has a density and a sound velocity essentially the same as those of the mantle. It is the most likely candidate in the search for the true mantle.

For the purpose of this discussion, the most important property of the mantle is its radioactivity, primarily from potassium and traces of uranium and thorium. It is convenient to express these concentrations in terms of the equivalent concentration in chondritic meteorites, for there are reasons to believe that, except for hydrogen and the noble gases, chondritic meteorites pretty well reflect the primordial abundances of the elements.

If a sample of peridotite represents a piece of the mantle, as we are assuming, analysis of the sample for radioactive elements will give us important data. St. Paul's Rock may be more representative of the mantle than a xenolith would be, for the xenolith must have been in contact with hot magma for a considerable period of time. Relative to chondritic meteorites, a sample from St. Paul's Rock was found[25] to be deficient in potassium by a factor of 0.1. Peridotite in general is known to have a very low abundance of thorium and uranium, though the data are scanty. No thorium or uranium was obtained in the analysis of St. Paul's Rock.

Radioactive elements might be expected to occur in the core and crust of the earth as well as in the mantle. Direct observation of the core is impossible. If we assume that the core is composed of metallic iron and nickel, we would not expect it to contain the chemically active elements thorium and uranium—elements which would combine with the silicates of the mantle. This conclusion is supported by the virtual absence of these elements among the metallic components of meteorites.

MacDonald[26] has discussed carefully what is known about radioactivity in the earth's crust. It is of interest that the amounts of uranium and thorium in the crust appear to be from 40 to 80 per cent of the amounts expected for the whole earth, if the earth is of chondritic composition. However, the potassium content of the crust is only 17 per cent of the expected total for a chondritic earth. Apparently the earth is deficient in potassium, on the basis of the assumptions; the abundance is 0.3 that expected for a chondritic earth.

It is important to note that the uranium and thorium are concentrated mainly in the continental crust, the unit-area concentration being 10 times higher on the continents than under the seas. Similarly, the unit-area concentration of potassium is twice as high on the continents as under the seas.

These results concerning the distribution of heat-producing elements are given in Table 1.

On the basis of these assumed abundances, the present rates of heat production per unit of surface area can be calculated: they are given in Table 2 (row 5). It should be noted that, in the case of continental surfaces, the observed heat flow agrees well with the computed total.

While infrared transfer of heat is probably the dominant means of transfer in the lower mantle, apparently this is less important than thermal conductivity in the upper mantle. The depth of heat penetration is given by the expression $(K/\omega\rho c)^{1/2}$, which for a thermal conductivity of $K = 0.03$ joule per centimeter per second, specific heat of $c = 1.3$ joules per gram, and density of $\rho = 4$ grams per cubic centimeter, gives, for a period of $T = 2\pi/\omega = 4.10^9$ years, a heat diffusion distance

TABLE 1.

Mass of heat-producing elements

Layer	Uranium (10^{19} g)	Thorium (10^{19} g)	Potassium (10^{23} g)
Oceanic crust	0.3 – 0.6	1.2 – 3.1	3.5 – 3.8
Continental crust	2.5 – 4.6	7.7 – 17	4.6
Mantle			5.3
Total	2.8 – 5.2	8.9 – 20.1	13.4 – 13.7
Expected total (chondritic)	6.6	26.0	48.0

of 100 kilometers. It is apparent that with a heat conductivity as low as this, or even with a conductivity greater by an order of magnitude, convection is needed to transfer heat from the interior of the earth to the surface. It may be noted that, by subtracting the contribution of the mantle, one obtains a calculated heat flow (Table 2) for the continents of 33 to 57 ergs per square centimeter per second.

Apparently, it is reasonable to assume, for the chondritic earth model, a distribution of the assumed total uranium and thorium as follows; in the continental crust, 65 per cent; in the oceanic crust, 7 per cent; in the mantle, or missing, 27 per cent.

The continental crust is sufficiently thin for the heat produced there to reach the surface by conduction. However, the large value for heat flow through the ocean floor is something of a mystery. If the foregoing assumptions concerning the distribution of radioactivity are correct, this heat cannot arise in the oceanic crust but must have its origin deep in the mantle. However, convection is required to remove the heat from deep within the earth's interior.

Some of the evidence for mantle convection has already been discussed. It should be noted here that these observations suggest that there are rising mantle

TABLE 2

Heat production per unit surface area.

Source	Oceanic surface (erg/cm² sec)	Continental surface (erg/cm² sec)
Uranium in crust	1 – 2	14 – 25
Thorium in crust	1 – 2	11 – 24
Potassium in crust	4	8
Potassium in mantle	4	4
Total	10 – 12	37 – 61
Observed (average)	50	50

currents under the mid-ocean ridges and falling currents under the continents or continental margins. Thus, such currents would be transferring heat to the oceanic surfaces in areas where the observed values are substantially in excess of the computed flux from the crust.

The source of this heat, transported by convection, is another question. Presumably either this heat must be produced in the mantle or core by radioactivity or the earth's interior must be cooling off, perhaps with the release of heat of crystallization. If, instead of being relatively steady, the convection should be impulsive, occurring periodically for relatively short periods, the heat from radioactive elements would be stored for perhaps many tens of millions of years before being transported to the surface. Since there is no evidence of a violent upheaval of the earth in the past, I will assume here that convection has been at a relatively steady rate.

The physical conditions to be satisfied in order for convection to occur in this manner are somewhat different from the usual conditions for convective transport in a fluid. Usually one expects to find an adiabatic temperature gradient if convection occurs, a slight excess gradient being sufficient to provide an adequte heat flux. In this case, however, the adiabatic temperature curve for the mantle lies well below the melting-point curve, and one is dealing with a solid rather than a liquid. While a solid can flow as a liquid at temperatures well below its melting point, its Newtonian viscosity would be expected to be too high for Newtonian flow to be important. Rather, the mantle would be expected to flow only if a finite yield stress is exceeded. This yield stress is a sensitive function of temperature, increasing as the difference between temperature and melting temperature increases. It is reasonable to assume, therefore, that the condition for a quasi-steady convective heat transport from the mantle is that the temperature curve should lie close enough to the melting-point curve to cause the mantle to be mechanically weak, permitting convection with small stress differences. If this condition were not satisfied, the resulting large yield stress would be expected to freeze convection until large stress differences developed, if they did. However, the relief of these large stresses after the yield stress is exceeded would result in the production of a large amount of heat along the flow surfaces, resulting in the reduction of the yield stress. It seems likely that the earth would be unstable under these conditions and that impulsive and catastrophic convection of the mantle would result. Large blocks of the mantle might be expected to turn over in a very short time (geologically speaking).

The condition that the mantle temperature be only slightly less than the melting point need not hold near the surface, where heat can be transported by conduction, nor need it hold at the bottom of the mantle, where radiation transport may suffice.

It is difficult to formulate the details of the convective process, particularly to find a model for which convection could occur without the basic instability of the system resulting in a rapid overturn of the whole mantle. However, for purposes of calculating heat flow we can by-pass the great complications of this complex problem by making use of a simpleminded, almost "thermodynamic" argument to calculate the rate of flow of heat, as follows: If it is assumed that the convective transport is steady and that the temperature of much of the mantle must therefore lie below, but near, the melting point, heat loss is at that rate which will keep the temperature near the melting point. This carries the following implications: If the melting-point curve is fixed because of a fixed gravitational constant, the rate of heat loss is equal to the present total generation of heat in the interior. If gravitation is growing weaker, and internal pressure is decreasing, there is an additional heat loss having its origin in a cooling of the interior because of a decreasing melting temperature.

If we assume that all the internally produced heat is carried by convection to the oceanic crust, the contribution from the mantle, per unit surface area, is given by the value in Table 2 increased by a factor of 5/3, the ratio of the surface area of the earth to that of the oceanic crust. This represents a contribution from the mantle of 7 ergs per square centimeter per second, or a total of 13 to 15 ergs per square centimeter per second. This is to be compared with an observed average flux of 50 ergs per square centimeter per second. The agreement is not particularly good.

The argument can be improved somewhat by adding the heat that has its origin in a cooling interior, as a result of weakening gravitation. The mechanism has just been discussed. As the gravitational "constant" decreases, the pressure and melting point of the lower mantle decrease. The temperature of the mantle follows the melting point, resulting in heat transport to the oceanic crust. Assuming 3 parts in 10^{11} per year as the rate of decrease of G, Murphy and I[16] have computed that this mechanism should yield 15 ergs per square centimeter per second, a value which should be added to that for heat having its origin in internal radioactivity. This gives a total of 28 to 30 ergs per square centimeter per second.

No allowance was made for heat due to uranium and thorium in the mantle. Assuming a content of uranium and thorium in the continental crust necessary (together with the potassium) to provide the observed heat flow and assuming the same abundances of these elements that are found in the chondritic meteorites, we find that the uranium and thorium in the mantle and oceanic crust would yield a heat flow through the oceanic crust of about $4\frac{1}{2}$ ergs per square centimeter per second for uranium and for thorium, or a total of 9 ergs per square centimeter per second. Adding the mantle contribution to the total heat flow from the oceanic floor gives 37 to 39 ergs per square centimeter per second, a value which agrees fairly well with the observed values. It is doubtful that the heat-flow observations on the ocean floor represent a proper statistical sample, and the final discrepancy is probably not significant. If we assume the true mean heat flow from the ocean floor to be only 35 ergs per square centimeter per second, the effect of a decreasing gravitational constant represents almost half the total.

It must be emphasized that the foregoing discussion has a strong conjectural element; it cannot be otherwise until we know much more than we now do about the composition of the earth and its internal temperature distribution.

The Earth's Magnetic Field

While the details of the mechanism may not be completely clear, it is now generally agreed that the earth's magnetic field is generated in the earth's liquid core through a dynamo action driven by convection in the core.[29] As an adiabatic temperature gradient is necessary for convection, the minimum necessary heat flow from the core is given by the thermal conduction with an adiabatic temperature gradient. This heat flow is computed at 1.5 to 4.0×10^{19} ergs per second, depending upon the thermal conductivity and adiabatic gradient assumed for the core.[16] The heat required to drive the core as a heat engine to produce the magnetic field has been estimated by Verhoogen[27] as less than 8×10^{19} ergs per second. The total required heat flow may be taken to be 2 to 5×10^{10} ergs per second.

If the assumption of an iron-nickel core of meteoritic composition is correct, radioactivity can provide only about 5×10^{16} ergs per second—an amount completely negligible.

The densities of the inner and outer core derived from seismic observations suggest that the inner core is an iron-nickel solid phase obtained through the solidification of the outer core. Urey[30] has suggested that the heat of fusion released by the gradual growth of the inner core may be the source of heat required to drive the convection. The continuous release of heat from a growing core requires a gradual reduction in temperature. As a result, thermal heat is also released by the whole core. An analysis of the thermal and pressure balance indicates that these two contributions to the heat flow from the core are roughly equal and require a rate of temperature decrease, at the core boundary, of 0.7 to 1.9×10^{-15} degree Kelvin per second if 4×10^{19} ergs per second are to be released to the mantle by the core.[16]

If the temperature at the base of the mantle is assumed to lie near the melting point, the rate of change of this temperature as a result of decrease in the "constant" of gravitation can be computed from Uffen's[28] melting-point curves. These give the result that the rate of change of temperature of the core boundary (when a fractional rate of decrease for G $3/10^{11}$ per year is assumed) lies in the range 2 to 4×10^{-15} degree Kelvin per second.[16]

If radiative heat transfer is sufficiently effective at great depths in the mantle, the temperature may follow the variation of melting point at the intermediate depth of 1500 kilometers. In this case the rate of decrease of the temperature of the core boundary is 1.5 to 3×10^{-15} degree Kelvin per second.

This rate of decrease is slightly greater than is needed to maintain an adiabatic temperature gradient in the core. Thus, a decreasing gravitational constant would be expected to produce core convection, and the production of a magnetic field becomes a possibility.

Without a decreasing gravitational "constant," there are difficulties. Without the convective mechanism active in the mantle, the lower mantle, because of its radioactivity, would be expected to warm up rather than cool off. This is a common feature of all the conductive models computed by MacDonald.[26] However, with a steadily convecting mantle, the temperature of most of the mantle should stabilize near the melting point, and this should produce an essentially constant temperature in the core.

One possible, but unlikely, mechanism for convection in the core is based on the assumption that the core was initially much hotter than the lower mantle. It could still be cooling off rapidly enough to provide the necessary heat transfer. In order for this to be feasible, it must be assumed that heat is transported by conduction in the lower mantle, for convective transport would quickly bleed off the excess heat until the temperature of the core fell to the value demanded by the previously stated condition for convection.

If transport of heat in the lower mantle is conductive, it is easy to compute an approximate value for the initial excess temperature of the core that would be needed to allow heat leakage at the right rate after 4×10^9 years.

The rate of flow of heat from the core, S, after a time t is given by the approximate expression

$$S \simeq 2\pi r_c^2 \, (K\rho c/t)^{1/2} \, \Delta T \tag{10}$$

where K, ρ, and c are the heat conductivity, density, and specific heat, respectively, of the mantle, ΔT is the initial temperature difference between the core and the mantle, and r_0 is the core radius. Assuming the high value of thermal conductivity $K = 0.5$ joule per centimeter per second per degree, $c = 1.3$ joules per gram per degree Celsius, $\rho = 5$ grams per cubic centimeter, $S = 4.10^{12}$ joules per second, and $t = 10^{17}$ seconds gives a temperature difference ΔT of 1000°K. For the more moderate thermal conductivity of 0.1 joule per centimeter per second, the required temperature difference is 2200°K. It should be emphasized that this expression neglects the warming effect of the radioactivity of the mantle. To include this effect these temperature differences must be increased.

There is no obvious reason for such a large initial temperature difference, and it is concluded that if the assumed compositions of the core and mantle are correct and convection of the lower mantle does not occur, or occurs in a continuous manner, none of the obvious ways of obtaining enough heat from the core are adequate. However, the heat flow accompanying decreasing internal pressure does appear to suffice.

Surface Temperature of the Earth

It is supposed that the luminosity of the sun varies with the value of the gravitational constant, very probably being proportional to its 7th or 8th power;[6,7] when the sun was hotter, in the past, the earth's surface must have been warmer, and it is interesting to investigate this time dependence.[14]

The simplest assumption is that the mean temperature of the earth's surface is proportional to the 4th root of the solar radiation flux at the earth's surface. Thus, the absolute temperature should vary as $G^{2.5}$. There is an extra factor $G^{1/2}$, because the radius of the earth's orbit varies at G^{-1}. Using the variation of G with time that is given in Fig. 1 and assuming the present age of the universe to be 8.0×10^9 years, we obtain the simplified measure of the mean surface temperature of the earth that is plotted in Fig. 4.

Three effects were neglected in computing the curve of Fig. 4. Because of the effects of stellar evolution, the sun brightens as the hydrogen in its core is depleted. This effect was neglected. Also, the effect on the radiation balance of the earth of a varying water-vapor content was neglected. According to Opik,[31] because of this variation the rate of heat transfer from the earth varies as the 3.65th power of the surface temperature rather than as the 4th power. These two effects tend to cancel each other, and the curve in Fig. 4 is still applicable.

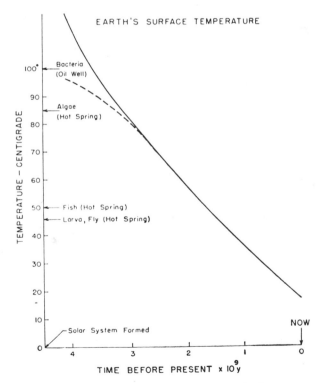

Fig. 4. The mean temperature of the earth in the past.

The third effect is probably more important. Should the surface temperature of the earth rise so high that the atmosphere was mostly water vapor, the convective mechanism of the atmosphere would be expected to change in such a way as to increase the earth's albedo, decreasing its temperature.

With the present atmosphere one would expect, and there is observed, a cloud cover of roughly 50 per cent associated with the 50 per cent of the surface that is occupied by rising air currents. However, with a water-vapor atmosphere, the cloud cover could be nearly complete, for rising water vapor could occur on most of the sunlit side of the earth, the water returning to the earth's surface as rain. The dashed curve in Fig. 4 represents the temperature corrected for this effect. The correction is based on the assumption that the earth's albedo rises to 0.55 when the surface temperature of the earth is 100°C.

The biological conditions essential for life apparently can be satisfied at these elevated temperatures.[14] The oldest extensive fossil evidence of life that we have is provided by the ancient algal reefs, some of which are over 10^9 years old. Apparently algae could have lived 3×10^9 years ago without violation of any conditions imposed by temperature requirements.

However, ancient glaciation may present a problem. Certainly it is difficult to believe that glaciation could have occurred 2.5×10^9 years ago with the mean temperature as high as 70° C. If completely reliable evidence for glaciation as long ago as this should be found—evidence that included glacial boulders and striated pavements as well as tillites—one would have to conclude that these high temperatures did not occur. The existence of an apparent tillite deposit by itself is probably not a positive indication of glaciation, as similar appearing conglomerates could be produced by other means.

The calculated temperature rise 6×10^8 years ago was so modest that glaciation at that time probably cannot be excluded.

It must be emphasized that the foregoing discussion cannot be marshaled as evidence for a gradual decrease in the gravitational constant. The earth is much too complex a system to be considered a reliable source of information to establish a physical theory. However, it is clear that the implications for the earth sciences of a gradually weakening gravitational interaction are far from trivial. The problems of the earth's magnetic field, heat flow, and expansion are all seriously affected. Even the biological sciences would be affected, for a high-temperature origin of life would be indicated under these conditions. What is badly needed to raise the discussion above the level of conjecture is a good demonstration that the gravitational constant has indeed been slowly decreasing.[32]

References and Notes to Appendix 9

[1] P. A. M. Dirac, *Proc. Roy. Soc.* (*London*), A **165**, 199 (1938).

[2] P. Jordan, *Schwerkraft und Weltall* (Vieweg, Brunswick, Germany, 1955); *Z. Physik*, **157**, 112 (1959).

[3] G. Ludwig, *Fortschritte der projektiven Relativitätstheorie* (Vieweg, Brunswick, Germany, 1951); K. Just, *Z. Physik*, **140**, 485 (1955);———, *ibid*, **141**, 592 (1955).

[4] C. Brans and R. H. Dicke, *Phys. Rev.*, **124**, 925 (1961); C. Brans, thesis, Princeton University (1961); ———, *Phys. Rev.*, **125**, 2194 (1962).

[5] P. Jordan, *Z. Physik*, **157**, 112 (1959); *Akad. Wiss. Lit.* (*Mainz*) *Abhandl. Math. Nat. Kl.*, **9**, 3 (1959); *Naturwissenschaften*, **11**, 417 (1961); *Astronaut. Acta*, **7**, 59 (1961).

[6] R. H. Dicke, *Rev. Mod. Phys.*, **29**, 355 (1957).

[7] ——, *Science in Space* (McGraw-Hill, New York, 1961), chap. 3; *Rev. Mod. Phys.*, **34**, 110 (1962).

[8] G. Berkeley, *A Treatise concerning the Principles of Human Knowledge* (1710).

[9] I. Newton, *Principia* (1687).

[10] R. H. Dicke, *Phys. Rev.*, **126**, No. 5 (1962) (see appendix 3).

[11] ——, *ibid.* **125**, 2163 (1962) (see appendix 2).

[12] J. Peebles and R. H. Dicke, *ibid.*, **127**, No. 2 (1962) (see appendix 6).

[13] R. H. Dicke, *Nature*, **194**, 329 (1962).

[14] E. Teller, *Phys. Rev.*, **73**, 801 (1948).

[15] G. Hess, thesis, Princeton University (1958).

[16] C. T. Murphy and R. H. Dicke, "The effect of a decreasing gravitational 'constant' on the interior of the earth," in preparation.

[17] T. J. Wilson, *Nature*, **185**, 880 (1960).

[18] B. C. Heezen, M. Tharp, M. Ewing, *Geol. Soc. Am. Spec. Papers, No. 65* (1959).

[19] S. W. Carey, *Continental Drift, A Symposium, Tasmania* (1958).

[20] L. Egyed, *Geophysica*, **7**, 13 (1960).

[21] W. A. Heiskanen and F. A. Vening Meinesz, *The Earth and Its Gravity Field* (McGraw-Hill, New York, 1958).

[22] W. H. Munk and G. J. F. MacDonald, *The Rotation of the Earth* (Cambridge Univ. Press, New York, 1960).

[23] H. Hess, in "Petrologic and Related Studies" (a volume in honor of A. F. Buddington). (Geological Society of America, New York, in press).

[24] ——, *J. Marine Res. (Sears Found. Marine Res.)*, **14**, 423 (1955).

[25] ——, private communication.

[26] G. J. F. MacDonald, *J. Geophys. Res.*, **64**, 1967 (1959).

[27] J. Verhoogen, *Am. Scientist*, **48**, 134 (1960).

[28] R. J. Uffen, *Trans. Am. Geophys. Union*, **33**, 893 (1952).

[29] W. M. Elsasser, *Phys. Rev.*, **72**, 821 (1947); E. C. Bullard, *Proc. Roy. Soc. (London)*, **A222**, 408 (1954).

[30] H. Urey, *The Planets, Their Origin and Development* (Yale Univ. Press, New Haven, Conn., 1952).

[31] E. J. Opik, "Climatic Change in Cosmic Perspective" (1961) (privately circulated).

[32] It is a pleasure to acknowledge the many suggestions and ideas I have derived from conversations with Professor H. Hess of the Princeton geology department. His help, as well as that of Professor H. D. Howland, with the details of the manuscript is also appreciated. This research was supported by research contracts with the Office of Naval Research and National Science Foundation.

Appendix 10
Implications for Cosmology of Stellar and Galactic Evolution Rates*
R. H. Dicke

Reprinted from *Reviews of Modern Physics*, Vol. 34 No. 1, 110–122, January, 1962

Introduction

Although it was not always so, physicists tend now to consider cosmology of little importance to them. They should remember, however, that the inertial-gravitational (or metric) field, and by implication cosmology, is basic to mechanics and concerns all branches of physics. Furthermore, there may be important space curvature factors helping to determine the structure of particles.[1,2]

* Supported in part by the Office of Naval Research and the United States Atomic Energy Commission.

Great progress has been made by astronomers in the past ten years on both the observational and theoretical aspects of the evolutionary history of the stars and our galaxy.[3] Recent results from these investigations have a considerable significance for cosmological and gravitational theories. This paper summarizes the current picture of stellar and galactic history and discusses its implications for cosmology and gravitational theory.

There are presently two classes of contending cosmologies, steady state[4,5] and evolutionary.[6] The steady-state cosmology is not compatible with general relativity as it requires continuous spontaneous mass generation in direct violation of the energy-momentum conservation laws as they appear in general relativity. The evolutionary cosmology is usually considered to be one of the possible models from general relativity. We shall consider here also two other evolutionary cosmologies, that of Dirac[7] and that of Brans and Dicke.[8] This latter theory as well as the steady-state cosmology were inspired by considerations of Mach's principle.[9]

It will be seen that the time of origin of the galaxy can be dated in several ways and that this pattern of ages is not self-consistent. Unfortunately, the various methods of dating the galaxy are not so firmly established that they can be accepted without question. However, some of the discrepancies are so large as to be disquieting, even to the experts who know the data best.

To anticipate a bit, it is difficult to see why globular clusters 25×10^9 years old should exist in an evolutionary universe of the closed type for which the age should be less than 9 billion years. It is also strange that certain galactic clusters should be older than the first heavy elements, as determined by uranium dating, even though these clusters have a very sizable amount of heavy element content. It is also strange that the evolutionary age of the galactic system, as determined by its rate of converting gas into stars, is at best only half the age of the globular clusters, a constituent part of the galaxy. All these points are discussed in some detail.

Stellar Evolution[10]

It has now become reasonably clear that our galaxy was formed originally as an enormous mass of highly turbulent hydrogen gas.[3] While the presence of some helium in the primordial gas cannot be easily excluded, there is little reason to believe that it was there. As for the heavier elements, there is direct observational evidence that they were substantially absent. The presence of well-defined classes of stars in the galaxy, each characterized by a particular spatial and velocity distribution and each having a different heavy element content, is ascribed to their formation at different times. It is presumed that there has been a continuous dirtying of the interstellar hydrogen medium by the elements formed in stellar interiors during advanced phases of stellar evolution and their subsequent discharge into the galactic gas through blow-off in novas or through other slower processes.

Heavy stars run through their life histories in a surprisingly short time (4×10^7 years for a star 10 times the sun's mass), first forming helium from hydrogen, then forming heavier elements from helium in a variety of processes. Consequently, many generations of these massive stars have added their heavy elements to the interstellar medium. The stars being generated now in the galaxy are formed from quite dirty gas containing roughly 4 per cent of elements heavier than helium, much of it in the form of dust grains, and a poorly known helium abundance of some 30 per cent by weight, the remainder being hydrogen. As the early evolution of a star appears to be normally unmixed, the composition of its outer envelope, as given by the stellar spectrum, is a measure of the original composition, hence old stars are indicators of the composition during early phases of the galaxy.

The indications are that stars usually, perhaps always, are formed in large groups, which may be gravitationally bound to form clusters, or unbound to form associations.[11] The stars of a cluster or association are apparently born almost simultaneously, seemingly through the fragmentation of a gas cloud.

Star clusters of all ages are found in the galaxy. The oldest are globular clusters each being gas free, containing up to 10^6 stars, and moving at high velocities. The stars of globular clusters appear to have a small heavy element content. Galactic clusters are found in the galactic disk, usually contain fewer stars than globular clusters, and range in age from very old ones to those formed "yesterday" in the spiral arms. Their stars contain a decidedly larger heavy element component.

The following summary of the life history of a star is based partly on observation, partly on theory reasonably well established. After the initial, little understood, condensation of a blob of gas to form a large proto star of low density, it contracts gravitationally, radiating away its gravitational energy. As this contraction takes place, the central temperature rises, varying inversely as the radius. Finally the central temperature reaches the point where the reactions

$$p + p \to d + e^+ + \nu$$
$$d + p \to \text{He}^3 + \gamma \tag{1}$$
$$\text{He}^3 + \text{He}^3 \to \text{He}^4 + p + p$$

are capable of converting hydrogen to helium. A light star (mass of the sun or less) then stops the continuous contraction and takes on a stable radius and temperature, the radiated energy now being obtained from the nuclear reactions. In this phase it occupies a point on the "main sequence" of the Hertzsprung–Russell diagram (Fig. 1). A star with a mass substantially greater than the sun requires so much energy to supply its radiation that it continues to contract until both the $p - p$ reaction and the carbon cycle

$$C^{12} + p \to N^{13} + \gamma$$
$$N^{13} \to C^{13} + e^+ + \nu$$
$$C^{13} + p \to N^{14} + \gamma$$
$$N^{14} + p \to O^{15} + \gamma \tag{2}$$
$$O^{15} \to N^{15} + e^+ + \nu$$
$$N^{15} + p \to C^{12} {}_\lambda \text{He}_4$$

are effective in converting hydrogen to helium. Thereafter it takes its stable place on the "main sequence."

A star lives on the main sequence, burning hydrogen at its center, until the available hydrogen in the core is exhausted ($\sim$ 15 per cent of its total hydrogen).

Thereafter, it starts to contract again, the temperature rising until hydrogen starts to burn in a shell outside the inert core. The inert core grows in size, and finally the central temperature rises until C^{12} is produced at the center of the star by the two-step process

$$He^8 + He^4 \rightleftarrows Be^8$$

$$Be^8 + He^4 \rightarrow C^{12} + \gamma. \tag{3}$$

This process is a precursor of many other types of nuclear reactions leading to the formation of the other elements. The onset of this contraction and the subsequent burning of hydrogen outside the core results in a star moving off the main sequence to form a red giant. This phase of its evolution, the subsequent nuclear reactions which result in the formation of heavy elements, and finally the process

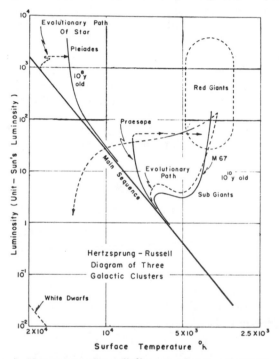

Fig. 1. Hertzsprung–Russell diagram of stellar distributions.

resulting in mass ejection (including, for a few stars, the catastrophic supernovas) may take relatively little time. Most of the life of a star is spent burning hydrogen while a member of the main sequence. To give typical values, a star 10 times the sun's mass might have a life time in the Kelvin contraction phase of the order of a hundred thousand years, burn hydrogen on the main sequence for 30 million years, and spend a few million years as a red giant before ejecting matter and undergoing metamorphism to a white dwarf.

A simple rough quantitative treatment of some of the factors involved in stellar evolution is easily given. This rough treatment is a reasonable approximation only for stars on the main sequence. Let the mass of the star be M, its radius be r, its central temperature be T_0, its surface temperature T_3, and its radiation rate (luminosity) be L.

The interior of a star must be hot to provide the high gas pressure necessary to support the outer parts. The virial theorem can be used to give an order of magnitude estimate of this central temperature. The average temperature of the star must satisfy the virial condition

$$R\langle T\rangle = -\tfrac{1}{3}\mu/M \times \text{(gravitational potential energy)}. \tag{4}$$

Here R is the gas constant and μ is the molecular weight of the gas (including free electrons) averaged over the whole star. The central temperature is then given approximately by

$$RT_0 \sim (GM/r)\mu. \tag{5}$$

The radiation energy density at the center is given by

$$(4\sigma/c)T_0^4, \tag{6}$$

with σ the Stefan–Boltzmann constant. The product of the radiation energy gradient, mean-free-path of radiation, and surface area determines the rate at which the star radiates.

$$L \sim T_0^4 r\sigma l. \tag{7}$$

Here l is the photon mean-free-path.

At very high temperatures and low densities the photon mean-free-path is determined by Compton scattering from the free electrons. However, for stars on the main sequence with a mass less than 10 times the sun's mass, the main scattering process when only hydrogen and helium are present is the inverse bremsstrahlung effect (free-free transition). When heavier elements are present, the effect of photo-ionization of bound electrons dominates. The photon scattering probabilities due to these two effects can be added to roughly give the following expression (Kramer's opacity) for the mean-free-path of a photon in a star,

$$l = \frac{10^{-25}}{g + 8 \times 10^{-3}}\, \rho^{-2}T^{3.5} \text{ cm}. \tag{8}$$

Here g is the fraction by weight of heavy elements ($Z > 2$) in the gas, and ρ is the density of the gas. In writing this equation the element distribution found in the sun for $Z > 2$ was assumed to be universal. In Equation (8), T and ρ can be taken to be approximately T_0 and Mr^{-3}, respectively. Combining with equation (7) and (5) gives

$$L = \frac{5 \times 10^{-31}}{(g + 8 \times 10^{-3})R^7}\, G^7 M^5 T_0^{1/2}\mu^7. \tag{9}$$

The numerical factor was modified to obtain rough agreement with more complete calculations and observations at the sun's mass.

When Compton scattering is the dominant photon scattering process, the mean-free-path varies inversely as the electron density and is temperature independent. For this case the luminosity of the star is proportional to the mass cubed and the gravitational constant to the fourth power. At the upper part of the main sequence, with a stellar mass of about 10 times the sun's mass, the Compton scattering is rather important and this effect shows up as a luminosity which increases with mass less rapidly than the 5th power.

Because of the critical dependence of nuclear reactions on the central temperature, T_0 may be considered as roughly constant and the luminosity is determined primarily by the mass of the star. This is particularly true for stars more massive than the sun, for they make use of the highly temperature-dependent carbon cycle for energy generation.

For such stars the equation for the main sequence can be obtained by assuming that the luminosity is proportional to approximately the 16th power of the central temperature, a reasonable value for the carbon cycle. As a first step, note that the surface temperature of a star satisfies

$$T_s{}^4 = L/4\pi\sigma r^2. \tag{10}$$

In equation (10), r can be eliminated using equation (5), replacing T_0 by its luminosity dependence, and combining with equation (9) to give the approximate relation

$$T_s \sim L^{3/16}(\mu G)^{1/5} \tag{11}$$

as the form of the main sequence in a plot of L against T_s as in the Hertzsprung–Russell diagram.

Ages of Stars

As equation (9) shows, for a given composition, the luminosity depends in a sensitive way only on the mass of a star, therefore it is a simple matter to calculate the time it stays on the main sequence once the fraction of hydrogen burned on the main sequence is known. This fraction can be calculated only with a detailed numerical integration and seems to be roughly 15 per cent, independent of the star's mass. This gives a lifetime on the main sequence for the sun of about 15×10^9 years. For very massive stars ($\sim 30 \times$ sun's mass) or stars with very little heavy element content, the amount of hydrogen burned may be as great as 30 per cent.

It might be thought that, being so close and well observed, the sun would have an evolutionary age, that is accurately known. Because of the term μ in equation (4), which contributes a factor μ^7 to the value of L [equation (9)], the luminosity increases as hydrogen is burned increasing the molecular weight. In principle the evolutionary age of the sun could be determined by measuring its luminosity. However, Schwarzschild[12] has pointed out that the initial helium abundance of the sun (as determined spectroscopically) is poorly known, and that this original helium also contributes to the mean molecular weight. Using possible values for the initial abundance of helium, the sun's evolutionary age could vary widely, perhaps from 4 to 15×19^9 years.

A star cluster has stars of various masses, but all having substantially the same age. It can have its evolutionary age determined, in principle, rather simply, provided it contains a large number of stars of all masses and provided all its stars were formed at substantially the same time. If the cluster is very young, its stars will fall on the main sequence in a Hertzsprung–Russel diagram. However, the life time of a star on the upper part of the main sequence is roughly proportional to M^{-2}. Hence, after a cluster has aged slightly, its massive (bright) stars will have evolved off the main sequence (see the star distribution for the Pleiades, Fig. 1). If the cluster is older than 10^9 years, its most massive stars will have already died and stars of a particular mass, (dependent upon age) will have become red giants. (See M67, Fig. 1). It should be noted that the age of a cluster can be determined simply by observing the color temperature of stars at the turnoff point on the main sequence.

Actually things are not quite this simple. Stars of intermediate mass burning hydrogen by the proton cycle, tend to evolve up the main sequence before they turn off. This can lead to a substantial error in the age of the very old clusters, for any small mistake in the calculation of the amount of brightening on the main sequence, before the "turn-off" affects the age strongly.

It is possible to obtain evolutionary ages for single stars which have evolved off the main sequence if their absolute luminosity is known. Knowing both the luminosity and color of a star allows its positioning on the Hertzsprung–Russell diagram. In addition, if its initial composition is known, from its spectrum, it can be positioned as a unique point on the evolutionary track describing the history of stars with its mass and initial composition. Knowing the composition enables its mass and age to be determined.

Recently Wilson[13] has developed a spectroscopic method for obtaining distances and absolute luminosities of stars wholesale. (Also see Oke[14]). The evolutionary ages of the older Wilston stars, the globular clusters, and a number of galactic clusters are given in Table I.[15] The uncertainty in the globular cluster ages should be regarded as at least 5 billion years and probably as large as 10 billion years.

As a measure of the reliability of these ages it must be reported that only 4 years ago the globular clusters were believed to be a rather uncertain 6 billion years old. At that time there began to appear distressing signs of trouble including the existence of a few stars (subgiants, Fig. 1) with a larger heavy element content

TABLE I

Stellar evolutionary ages

Object	Population (Table II)	Evolutionary age (10^9 yr)
Globular cluster	Halo	25
Galactic cluster NGC 188	Intermediate Population II or Disk?	16
Wilson stars	Intermediate Population II or Disk	12–15
Galactic cluster M67	Disk?	9
Sun (Radioactivity age 4.5×10^9 yr)	Disk	4–15
Hyades	Extreme Pop. I	1
Pleiades	Extreme Pop. I	0.1

(hence younger than globular clusters) which seem to be somewhat older than the globular clusters on the basis of stellar evolution. More recently a galactic cluster (NGC 188) has been found to have an age of about 16 billion years. At about the same time, it was also found that because of brightening on the main sequence, a substantial correction to the age of globular clusters was needed. Because of this substantial correction, their computed age is particularly sensitive to the value of this brightening. An improved integration gave roughly 25 billion years for the ages of the globular clusters. All these evolutionary ages are tabulated in the third column of Table I.

Because of the low heavy-element abundance in the globular clusters, they may be presumed to be among the oldest members of the galaxy. Having dated the oldest members we have a rough date for the time of origin of the galaxy. This can be compared with other methods of dating to be discussed.

Galactic Evolution

Having described the manner in which the age of individual stars and star clusters are determined, we turn to a discussion of the evolution of the galactic system and its age. While this may seem superficially similar to the stellar evolution problem, it is actually quite different. The evolutionary age of a star is determined by the rate it converts hydrogen in its interior to helium. However, the evolutionary age of the galactic system is determined by the rate at which hydrogen gas is converted into long-lived stars. It is interesting that the average luminosity of the galaxy in the sun's vicinity is rather insensitive to the stellar evolution rates, being determined largely by the galactic evolution rate. The reason for this is the very rapid evolution of the massive stars, the radiation in the vicinity of the sun being largely that from these short-lived bright stars. It matters not if they be twice as bright and live half as long. The average radiation density is unaffected.

The galaxy appears presently to contain roughly 2 per cent gas[16] (determined by observations of the 21-cm hydrogen line). The remainder of the matter is probably primarily in stars which can be divided roughly into three classes:

(1) A halo population consisting of very old stars with a large dispersion in velocity, very weak metal lines, and distributed almost spherically about the galactic center with a strong concentration toward the center.

(2) A disk population consisting of a smooth pancake distribution of stars having velocity dispersion only a 5th as great as the halo but twice that of young stars. These stars are old and have a substantial heavy element content. The sun may have a composition typical of the disk population.

(3) A spiral population consisting of a patchy spiral distribution of recently formed stars as well as somewhat older stars. The spiral lies coplanar with the disk population. Most of the gas is observed in the spiral structure and it is here that the short-lived bright blue stars are to be found now.

The stellar velocity distributions appear to mirror the distributions of turbulence velocities in the gas out of which they were formed. The relaxation time for star–star encounters to change the velocity distributions is enormous ($\sim 10^{14}$ years). While star encounters with gas clouds may be, and probably are, more effective,[17] they apparently do not suffice to change the dispersion in high-velocity stars greatly. Star velocities perpendicular to the galactic plane much greater than 10 km/sec are probably affected but slightly by cloud encounters.[16] The relaxation time[18] for gas turbulence to die out is now, and may always have been, less than 2×10^8 years. If it is assumed that the very large velocities of halo stars resulted from a primordial turbulence in the original gas mass, a turbulence which quickly decayed with time, it is possible that the whole of the halo population formed in less than 2×10^8 years. It also appears that roughly 25–50 per cent of the heavy element content of the galaxy was formed in this short time. If this were not so, with the above assumptions, a class of moderate velocity stars would be found having a very low heavy element content.

However, it is also possible that stellar radiation may have driven the gaseous turbulence, and produced and maintained these high turbulence velocities for a substantially longer period than 2×10^8 years. This is discussed later.

It is believed that collisions between gas clouds is the dominant mechanism for dissipating turbulence. With the cloud velocities and densities typical of the solar vicinity now, these collision rates are about 1 per 10^7 years. The collisions should be quite inelastic, the heat being radiated away by the gas. However there is one quite uncertain factor. Magnetic fields in the clouds and intercloud medium would serve as elastic bumpers to make $\frac{2}{3}$ of the collisions somewhat elastic. Even with quite large values of the magnetic field (2×10^{-5} gauss) the relaxation time[18] is not likely to exceed 2×10^8 years.

After the initial large decrease in velocity dispersion, which may represent the decay of primordial turbulence, a steady progression to lower dispersion velocities with increase in the time of formation appears to be a well defined property of the stellar distribution. This also may be due to higher gaseous turbulence velocities in the past because of a greater luminosity of stars in the galaxy driving the gaseous turbulence. This possibility is also discussed later.

It is possible and convenient, to make a finer division into stellar population than the crude threefold separation described above. Five different stellar populations are described in Table II. This table is based on an article by Oort[16] which incorporates the ideas and measurements of many people. The table in Oort's article has been modified somewhat by combining the two disk populations into a single population. In this table the average velocity and distance from the galactic plane are not always independently observed results. All the values are rather strongly conditioned by values in the solar neighborhood and may not be good galactic averages. The heavy element assignments[19] are somewhat arbitrary but appear to be fairly consistent with the observed present hydrogen-gas abundance and the observed heavy-element abundance. The mass assigned by Oort to intermediate population II and the disk population has been divided between the two.

To be self-consistent, the mass assignments should be such that the total mass of heavy element generated by the short-lived component of a given population appear in the gas and stars of the next population. This mass can be computed roughly as the increase in the fractional abundance of heavy elements times the mass of the galaxy that is not yet condensed into stars. These products are given in line 6 of Table II. For consistency these numbers should be proportional to the population masses (line 4). It is seen that they are reasonably self-consistent.

TABLE II

Stellar populations

Population Some typical members	Halo population II Globular clusters RR Lyr. var. with period > 0.3 d	Intermediate population II High velocity stars (F-M). Long period variations	Disk population Planetary nebulas, bright red giant novas. Weak line stars	Intermediate population I. Strong line stars	Extreme population I Gas, supergiants
Average distance from galactic plane (parsecs)	2000	700	300	160	120
Average velocity (V_z) perpendicular to galactic plane	75 km/sec	25	15	10	8
Mass in unit of 10^9 suns	16	30	17	5	2
Heavy elements ($Z > 2$), fractional by weight (Schwarzschild)	0.003	0.01	0.02	0.03	0.04
Heavy element produced: mass in unit of 10^9 suns	0.21	0.39	0.26	0.09	0.04
Mass of gas when population was first formed	71.5	55.5	25.5	8.5	3.5
Calculated (V_z) from equation (16) km/sec	38	24	15	12	9

By making use of Salpeter's ideas, a time scale can be added to Table I. Salpeter[20] concluded from a study of stellar magnitude distributions, in the sun's vicinity, that the stellar formation rate, as a density, is simply proportional to the average gas density. Assuming that this is valid for all parts of the galaxy, the heavy element fractional abundance of the gas increases roughly linearly with the time, and the amount of gas decreases approximately exponentially. From Table I it is evident that with the exception of the first, or halo population, roughly equal time intervals of formation should be assigned to the various populations.

On physical grounds, Salpeter's assumption, that the stellar formation rate, per unit gas mass is independent of gas density, is less promising than Schmidt's[21] assumption that the formation rate increases with increased gas density. Certainly one would expect a density dependence if cloud collision plays a role in stellar formation. However, both assumptions are compatible if the gas density has been approximately constant in time. This appears to be supported slightly by the observations. As determined from the present distribution of high velocity stars, the volume occupied by the gas when the intermediate population II was formed was very roughly 1×10^{12} cubic parsecs, and the volume of gas in the spiral arms[22,23] is now roughly 6×10^{10}. These volumes are in substantially the same ratio as the gas masses given in line 8, Table II.

With the assumption that the turbulence velocity increases with luminosity, there exists a regulatory mechanism tending to keep the gas density constant. An increased density would lead to an increased stellar creation rate per unit volume. This in turn would increase the turbulence velocities and expand the gas reducing the stellar creation rate. It should be recognized that by gas expansion one means here increased separation between gas clouds, not a change in the gas density within a cloud. By treating individual gas clouds as molecules, the virial theorem may be used to relate the cloud distribution to the translational and rotational kinetic energy of the clouds (i.e., turbulence kinetic energy) even though the turbulence is so heavily damped that arguments involving equipartition are not valid.

For a flattened galaxy composed principally of gas clouds, the Maxwellian velocity distribution would lead to a relatively small variation in cloud density for 70 per cent of the gas lying in a column perpendicular to the galactic plane. Thus even spatially the density of gas clouds may have been relatively constant in the galaxy.

This was probably not true of the gas distribution which preceded the halo population, however, as the nearly spherical distribution requires a strong concentration toward the center. This raises the interesting question of whether central cloud densities and stellar formation rates might not have been very great while the halo population was being formed. We shall return to this question.

A pivotal question in the above discussion is whether the turbulence velocity does in fact depend upon galactic radiation in the correct way. The various possible ways of driving turbulence in the galactic gas have been discussed by Oort and Spitzer,[23] and by Spitzer.[18]

Unfortunately, the physical state of the interstellar medium is not known with great reliability and the following discussion is somewhat tentative. In the spiral arms of the galaxy, the hydrogen gas is found primarily in clouds of various types. If all these clouds are assumed identical, the best fit with the bulk of the observations is obtained if the density is taken to be 10 neutral hydrogen atoms per cm^3, the radius 7 parsecs, and the mass 400 solar masses. There are then 5×10^4 of these clouds per 10^9 parsecs^3. The gas in the clouds is at a temperature of $100\,°K$ in contrast to the inter-cloud medium which is believed to be at a temperature of roughly $10^4\,°K$. The density of the intercloud medium is believed to be 0.05 atoms/cm^3 giving a pressure equal to that in the clouds.[18]

Unfortunately the strength of the interstellar magnetic field is not known with any reliability and it may be important to an understanding of gas turbulence. Indirect observations of several different types[18] suggest a field strength of about 2×10^{-5} gauss, but it may be as weak as 10^{-6} gauss.

Of the various ways by which gaseous turbulence can be driven by the radiation, the most important effect for obtaining high cloud velocities may be a gas pressure propulsion of the cloud by the sudden expansion of surface layers on one side of the cloud as a result of its sudden exposure to the radiation from a newly formed massive star.[23] Such stars are very hot and the ultraviolet radiation quickly eats its way into the neutral cloud, ionizing the side facing the star and raising the temperature of the gas to roughly $10^4\,°K$. This process stops when the thickness of the ionized layer is sufficiently great for the absorption of the radiation through the ionization of recombined atoms. The pressure in the ionized gas is 200 times as great as in the remainder of the interstellar medium and it quickly expands into the intercloud medium. At this stage there is considerable uncertainty as to what should happen.

If the magnetic field is sufficiently weak, the gas cloud should simply recoil as a rocket, and this is the case considered by Oort and Spitzer.[23] However, if the magnetic field is as strong as 2×10^{-5} gauss and is directed perpendicular to the line joining the cloud and star, the bubble blown in the field by the expanding ionized gas should have important effects. Most of the work done by the expanding gas is stored in the magnetic field energy. Because of the resulting distortion of the magnetic field around the bubble the pressure in the interior exceeds that in the normal cloud. Also, because of the unsymmetrical shape of this greatly expanded bubble, this excess pressure acts partially upon the neutral cloud. One can visualize the bubble thereafter displacing the cloud and emptying through gas loss along the magnetic field lines.

This mechanism is very complex, and a proper calculation has not been made, so conclusions are not firm. However, an estimate indicates that for the evaporation of a small fraction of a slowly moving cloud (~ 5 per cent) the momentum recoil from this magnetic pressure may exceed the rocket effect by a factor of 2. At high cloud velocities, in a direction away from the bright star, the effect appears to be unimportant.

Under given radiation conditions the reaction force acting on a cloud should be proportional to its area. Hence, assuming some standard gas density in the cloud, the acceleration is almost independent of the cloud mass, varying as $M^{-1/3}$. To simplify matters this mass dependence will be neglected.

In order to obtain a rough idea as to the dependence upon stellar parameters of the turbulence velocity, we neglect the velocity dependence of jet propulsive forces which would be associated with strong magnetic fields, if they exist. We note that a bright hot star appears to be surrounded by a central field of force, and that a cloud encountering a star already luminous is merely scattered without a change in its squared velocity. If, however, the star suddenly becomes luminous when the cloud is close, work is done on the cloud through the repulsive force as the cloud moves away. If the extinction of a star is as precipitous, the effect of stars turning off would tend to cancel the effect of their turning on. However, the cooling of stars, as they move into the giant branch, may be more gradual than their initial brightening.

If Δv^2 represents the mean increase in the average v^2 per massive star which brightens close enough to the cloud to be significant, the mean rate of increase of v^2 with time, neglecting damping effects is

$$dv^2/dt = \tfrac{4}{3}\pi R^3 n_s \Delta v^2,\tag{12}$$

where n_s is the density rate at which such stars appear and R is the maximum range at which such stars are effective. The rate of change due to damping by inter-cloud collisions is

$$dv^2/dt = -\alpha v^3 l^{-1}.\tag{13}$$

Here l is the appropriately defined mean-free-path for cloud encounters and α is the damping constant, less than unity, and dependent upon the magnetic field strength. Combining equations (12) and (13) gives for the mean equilibrium cloud velocity

$$v = (\tfrac{4}{3}\pi \alpha l R^3 n_s \Delta v^2)^{1/3}.\tag{14}$$

Here v is the root-mean-cube velocity computed as an average without regard to the mass of the cloud. Weighted by the cloud's mass, the average would be somewhat less, for the rapidly moving clouds would be rapidly moving only as a result of a previous substantial evaporation of gas.

With the assumption that average gas densities, and stellar creation densities have been substantially constant during the life of the galaxy, it is not unreasonable to suppose that this also implies no drastic change in the average cloud size and density.

With Salpeter's[20] assumptions, v should be time independent, for he assumes that the stellar creation function is time independent. Thus n_s is proportional to cloud density, and the product n_{sl} is time independent.

In order to obtain a time dependent v without ruining the fabric of Salpeter's theory, one might assume a time dependence at the luminous end of the creation function. If luminous stars were more probably in the past, equation (14) would lead to a larger v in the past.

An interesting alternative explanation is provided by the cosmologies with a time varying gravitational constant, for with the gravitational constant greater in the past all stars are brighter. From equation (9) the luminosity of a star varies as the 7th power of the gravitational constant. This result is based upon the Kramer's opacity law, equation (8). For the very heavy stars which are most important for the propulsion of the gas clouds, Compton scattering is more important than the photo effect. If the opacity were due completely to Compton scattering, the luminosity would be expected to vary as G^4. We shall assume a variation as the 5th power to make allowance for some photo-absorption. While the gravitational constant should enter also into other factors effecting cloud dynamics and stellar creation, we shall assume that such effects do not depend in a sensitive way on G.

In order to include the effect of a changing gravitational constant upon v in equation (14), we note that an increase of the brightness of all stars by a factor of 4 increases R in equation (14) by a factor of 2 (neglecting absorption by the intercloud medium). Δv^2 in equation (14) also scales by a factor R because it is given by a force per unit mass times a displacement, which scales as R. Hence, v varies as the (luminosity)^{2,3}.

As it is only the radiation beyond the Lyman limit of hydrogen which is effective in ionizing hydrogen, it is necessary to consider separately the effect of increase in the area of a star and in its surface temperature in calculating the brightening of the star in the appropriate part of the spectrum. From equation (5), the area increases as G^2 and the surface temperature increases as $G^{3/4}$. For a star with $T_s = 63\,300\,°K$, and the appropriate part of the spectrum, the radiation intensity increases as roughly $T_s^{4.5}$. This results in this part of the radiation intensity varying with G as $G^{5.4}$. Inserting this result in equation (14) gives

$$v \sim G^{3.6}. \tag{15}$$

This relation contains no correction for the increased plasma temperature which would result from bluer radiation. If it could be presumed that this correction to Δv^2 in equation (14) should be proportional to the stellar temperature change, equation (15) becomes modified only slightly to become

$$v \ G^{3.9}. \tag{16}$$

As it seems likely that the correction is even less than this, it will be neglected.

To anticipate a bit, it will be found that the cosmology which best eliminates the discordant age pattern is that of Brans and Dicke.[8]

Using the detailed numerical integration of the cosmological solution giving the ages tabulated in the last column of Table III, one obtains G as a function of time. These values of G are substituted in equation (15) to give the values of v tabulated in the last row of Table II. These velocities were adjusted to agree with observations for the disk population. It was assumed that the halo population was formed in 2.5×10^8 years at the start of expansion of the universe with the remaining time divided equally between the four other periods of galactic evolution. A comparison with observations (Table II) shows good agreement, too good, for all populations except the halo where primordial turbulence, if it existed, would be expected to invalidate the relation.

It is possible that the large velocities in the halo population may not represent a dying primordial turbulence but rather a turbulence stirred by stellar radiation. As was indicated previously, the nearly spherical gas distribution, assumed as the precursor of the halo population, would require a strong concentration of gas clouds toward the center and the cloud density could not be constant (spatially) without very large turbulent velocities near the center. It seems likely under these circumstances that in the central region the density would be great, stellar formation rate densities great also, and turbulence velocities high. Thus Salpeter's assumptions would probably be invalid until the galactic disk had flattened sufficiently to permit a relatively constant gas density throughout the disk.

To summarize, one may feel a certain cautious optimism about Salpeter's hypothesis. Although his conclusion that the stellar creation rate is simply proportional to the amount of gas in the galaxy was based on a study of the luminosity function for stars in the solar neighborhood only, its validity seems to be of wider significance. The mass assignments are in agreement with the assumed values of the abundance of hydrogen gas and the fractional heavy-element abundance. Of course it should be emphasized that these masses are but poorly known. Also, and perhaps more significant, is the fact that the density of hydrogen gas seems not to have changed drastically with time. This makes the assumptions of Schmidt and Salpeter compatible. Even the puzzling higher turbulence velocity in the past, necessary to keep the gas density approximately constant, could conceivably be explained.

We tentatively accept Salpeter's model and turn now to calculation based on his idea of the age of the galaxy.

Evolutionary Age of the Galaxy

As a first step in calculating an evolutionary age of the galaxy, the mean life of the gas is computed. Stellar evolution provides the time scale for this calculation but it should be emphasized that it is the young relatively short-lived stars that provide the time scale not the ancient ones. Thus the unit of time is set by stellar conditions now and not by what they were in times long past. For this reason effects of a gravitational constant possibly varying with time can probably be ignored.

By observing the brightness distribution among stars in a very young galactic cluster, the luminosity distribution of stars newly created is obtained.[24] This distribution we define as the Salpeter creation function.[20] This distribution function is defined as the number of stars in the distribution having a given visual magnitude per unit magnitude. The luminosity function per unit volume for stars in the solar neighborhood differs from the luminosity function of young clusters (creation function) because the only short-lived stars present in the solar neighborhood are those created a relatively short time ago. Consequently the luminosity function for the brighter stars gives a direct measure of their creation rate, once their stellar evolutionary life times are known. Also, knowing the creation function, the total present star creation rate is known.

The Salpeter creation function plus a knowledge of stellar evolutionary life times enables the mortality rate for stars newly formed to be calculated. The result is that 25 per cent of the mass of a star cluster dies in the first 5×10^8 years. It is presumed that roughly 80 per cent of this matter returns to the galactic gas and that the remaining 20 per cent is composed of white dwarfs. In the next half-billion years only 7 per cent more deaths occur and perhaps $\frac{2}{3}$ of this appears as rejuvenated gas. It is possible that only half the 7 per cent of the original gas mass that dies in the next 1.7×10^9 years is returned to the interstellar medium. The next 20×10^9 years of stellar evolutionary life can account for only 22 per cent more mass loss of which the amount of rejuvenated hydrogen gas might be only $\frac{1}{5} \times 22$ per cent $= 4$ per cent.

These values are based on the luminosity function and creation function given by Sandage.[24] This luminosity function may not be reliable for stars of low luminosity. There are apparently serious observational difficulties connected with studies of such dim stars.

The bulk of the reincarnated galactic gas returned into the interstellar medium is materialized in the first 10^9 years after a star cluster is formed and for purposes of a rough calculation one can treat this regurgitation process as instantaneous; also, for a rough calculation, one can neglect the gas produced after the first billion years.

With this simplifying assumption, the galactic gas decreases exponentially with time (after the rapid formation of the halo population). To give a specific example of the way the mean life for this exponential decay is calculated using the Salpeter creation function and the luminosity function of the field stars, we consider the density of stars whose absolute visual magnitude falls in the range -1.5 to -2.5 in the vicinity of the sun. From the luminosity function[24] it is found to be $4.8 \times 10^{-6}/(\text{parsec})^3$. Such stars have an average life (calculated) for 4×10^7 years.[10] Combining these two results gives the fairly reliable creation rate of $1.2 \times 10^{-13}/(\text{parsec})^3$ yr. Combining this with the observed creation function,[24] gives a rate of formation of stars of all magnitudes of $5.5 \times 10^{-11}/(\text{parsec})^3$ yr averaged over the last 4×10^7 years. This corresponds to 2.6×10^{-11} solar masses$/(\text{parsec})^3$ yr. The average density of hydrogen gas in the solar neighborhood is roughly 0.025 solar masses$/(\text{parsec})^3$. This density is calculated from radio telescope observations.

Not all the hydrogen gas converted to stars is permanently lost. From the preceding discussion, roughly 25 per cent may be assumed to be returned quickly

(10^9 years) to the gas medium. Hence the rate of gas lost may be taken to be 2.0×10^{-11} solar masses/(parsec)^3 yr. Combining this with the gas abundance gives 1.3×10^9 years for the mean life of the gas. This should be considered a lower limit since the correction for optical thickness in the determination of the hydrogen-gas abundance may be too small, perhaps by a factor[16] as great as 1.5. Also the amount of hydrogen returned to the gas by bright stars may be as great as 45 per cent. The mean life may consequently be taken to lie in the range 1.3–2.6×10^9 yr.

The present fractional content of gas in the spiral arms of the galaxy is 2 per cent. Combining with the above mean life times gives a galactic age in the range of 5.0–10.0×10^9 yr. A correction to this age is needed for the effect of hydrogen gas being returned to the interstellar medium by the decay of long lived stars. This correction cannot be made with assurance as the fraction of the mass of the dwarf star ejected as gas is not known. Assuming a mean life of 1.9×10^9 years, and that all the material is returned, one finds an upper limit to the correction of $+1.3$ billion years. It is apparently negligible compared with the other uncertainties. It is also possible that there is a considerable amount of gas locked up in ionized form in the halo, this gas being returned to the disk in the central part and spiraling outward along the spiral arms. If this were true, the gas depleted phase of the galaxy might be stretched, somewhat increasing its age. It is doubtful that such a stretch-out could amount to more than 2 billion years or Salpeter would have obtained a quite different interpretation of the luminosity function. The galactic evolutionary age is finally in the range 5–12×10^9 years.

The Age of Uranium

Still another way of dating the galaxy is to make use of the decay of uranium. The theory of formation of uranium with the r process[25] is sufficiently well defined that it is possible to compute a formation ratio

$$[U^{235}]/[U^{238}] = 1.56. \tag{18}$$

If one were confident of the formation history of this element, one should be able to obtain a quite good value for the age of the galaxy.

Fowler and Hoyle[26] assume an exponentially decreasing formation rate, basing their assumption on Salpeter's theory.[20] However, as we have seen, the fractional heavy element abundance would be expected to increase linearly with time (after the initial halo production of about 1 per cent). (On the other hand see note 19 regarding the latest observational evidence on these abundances.)

From the previous discussion, and assuming the correct mass assignment to the halo population, the halo population represents the remnants of the initial fragmentation into stars of almost $\frac{1}{2}$ of the galaxy. Of this mass, it is expected that 25 per cent was regurgitated in 0.5×10^9 years to contribute 1 per cent heavy elements to the gas mass.

These conclusions depend upon three assumptions:
(1) The mass of the halo population and the heavy element abundance are reasonably correct.
(2) The Salpeter creation function is applicable to the halo population.
(3) The ratio of the amount of uranium produced to the hydrogen gas processed by the stars is constant.

This last assumption is not in accord with the more detailed conditions of Fowler and Hoyle[26] who assume that uranium is made in type I supernovas and that these supernovas represent the end of stars having an evolutionary life of 3–4 × 10⁹ years, necessitating such a delay in the production of uranium. The advanced evolutionary phases of stars are not believed to be sufficiently well understood at present to warrant firm conditions as detailed as these. Furthermore, with the Dirac and Brans–Dicke cosmologies, stars evolve rapidly at the beginning of the galaxy, and the waiting period becomes negligibly short. More serious is the fact that the observations now suggest that the halo population produced 50 per cent of the heavy element content (see reference 19).

With the above assumptions, the time rate of change of the fractional abundance of heavy elements becomes

$$dg/dt = [\delta(t) + 3/T] \times 10^{-2}. \tag{19}$$

Here the delta function represents the prompt contribution from the halo population and T is the present age of the galaxy.

To take account of the possibility that the prompt production of uranium by the halo population[19] may have been as great as 50 per cent, we shall calculate also with the 3 in equation (19) replaced by 1.

At the time of formation of the solar system (4.5 × 10⁹ years ago), the relative abundance of an element undergoing radioactive decay was:

$$[\ ] = \int_0^{-4.5} e^{-\gamma(T-4.5-t)} \frac{dg}{dt}\, dt. \tag{20}$$

Here λ^{-1} is the mean life of the element. Applying these equations to U²³⁵ and U²³⁸ gives

$$\frac{[U^{235}]}{[U^{238}]} = 1.6 \frac{3T_5 + (T - 3T_5)\exp[-(T-4.5)T_5^{-1}]}{3T_8 + (T - 3T_8)\exp[-(T-4.5)T_8^{-1}]} \tag{21}$$

for the abundance ratio at the time the earth was formed. Here $T_5 = 1.03$ billion years and $T_8 = 6.5$ billion years represent the two men lives of U₂₃₅ and U₂₃₈ respectively. The present abundance ratio is

$$[U^{235}]/[U^{238}] = 7.2 \times 10^{-3}. \tag{22}$$

This implies that the abundance ratio was 0.29 when the earth was formed 4.5 billion years ago. Setting the ratio given by equation (21) equal to 0.29 allows T to be determined. The result is $T = 11.1 \times 10^9$ years for the age of first formation. The time of first formation might reasonably be taken as giving an age of the galaxy. This result depends upon the amount of prompt production of heavy element assumed for the initial population. If the initial prompt production were assumed to be as great as 50 per cent the resulting age of the galaxy becomes 7.5 billion years. We finally adopt the range 7.5–11.1 × 10⁹ years for the age of the galaxy as dated by uranium.

The Evolutionary Age of the Universe

For the evolutionary cosmologies, the age of the universe is determined from the expansion rate, observed as a Doppler shift in the light received from the receding galaxies. The Hubble age of the universe is the average of the values of distance divided by recessional velocity for the galaxies not too far away. As is usual nowadays, the cosmological term in Einstein's field equation is dropped. It is easily verified that the age of the universe must be less than or equal to the Hubble age.[27] Also for the closed universe, which on philosophical grounds is most satisfactory, the universe must be less than or equal to $\frac{2}{3}$ the Hubble age.

For Dirac's cosmology[7] the age of the universe is $\frac{2}{3}$ the Hubble age and for the Brans–Dicke[8] cosmology with a closed universe, less than or equal to this value.

The Hubble age accepted now is approximately 13 billion years. While confidence in this number on the part of the experts has gained considerable strength in the last couple of years, the nonexperts will want to bear in mind that this important number was 2 billion years a decade ago and that the change resulted from finding errors in interpretation of the original data as well as from new data.

While the age of the universe is infinity for the steady-state cosmology and need not be considered, there is another age which is significant. Averaged over a large enough volume, all classes of objects have the same mean age, $\frac{1}{3}$ the Hubble age. Thus the mean age of all galaxies should be 4.3×10^9 years.[4,5] Also the age distribution should be exponential so that only 0.3 per cent of the galaxies would have an age of 25×10^9 years or more. It should be noted, however, that our galactic system seems in no way unusual. It is a typical spiral, the most common type of galaxy. The galactic system is a member of a cluster of galaxies, the local group, which being gravitationally bound would be expected to have a common age. These galaxies appear typical. In particular the elliptical galaxies have a color distribution typical of the color distribution normal to elliptical galaxies as a whole.

It has often been remarked that the spread in color of elliptical galaxies as a class is small. The color distribution seems to be quite similar to that of the galactic cluster M67. By relating the age determination to that of M67 Crampin and Hoyle[28] get for the age distribution of elliptical galaxies 10–16×10^9 years, lying well outside the value 4.3×10^9 years expected from the steady state universe.

It is possible that elliptical galaxies may be second generation galaxies, with spirals evolving into elliptical after the gas is substantially exhausted.[29] However, the nebular class S_0 is a better candidate for this dubious distinction, as it exhibits the smooth distribution of dwarf stars expected to remain in the spiral arms, with the spiral arm structure smoothed out.[30] There is also a difficulty with the abundance. Taking the mean age of ellipticals to be 13 billion years, the present abundance of elliptical galaxies (15 per cent) is possible for the steady-state cosmology with an average age of 13×10^9 years only if all spiral galaxies evolve into ellipticals.

Cosmological Consideration

The various age determinations discussed above have been summarized in the first four columns of Table III. It is evident that there are serious discordances. The age of the globular clusters is 3 times the maximum age of a closed evolutionary universe. Old galactic clusters are older than the heavy elements they contain. The globular clusters are older than the galactic system which contains them.

While one of these difficulties is not present for the continuous creation universe, the others remain and, as discussed above, new ones are added.

The two place accuracy of Table III is certainly a joke. Considering the changes which have taken place in these numbers in the past 10 years, other changes should

TABLE III

Age (in unit 10^9 years).

Object	Type of age	General relativity	Continuous creation	Dirac cosmology	Brans–Dicke $A_0 \gg 13$ billion years $\omega = 4.5$	Brans–Dicke $A_0 \gg 13.0$ $\omega = 6.0$	(Positive curvature) Brans–Dicke $A_0 = 15.0$ $\omega = 6.0$
Globular cluster	Stellar evolution	$\Delta t = \Delta t^* = 25$	$\Delta t = \Delta t^* = 25$	$\Delta t = 3.4$	$\Delta t = 8.1$	$\Delta t = \ldots$	$\Delta t = 7.8$
Old galactic cluster NGC 188	Stellar evolution	16	16	2.9	7.5	8.0	7.0
Sun	Stellar evolution	4–15	4–15	1.8–2.9	3.0–7.4	3.2–7.9	2.5–6.9
Sun	Radioactivity	4.5	4.5	4.5	4.5	4.5	4.5
Galactic system	From depletion of hydrogen gas	5–12	5–12	5–12	5–12	5–12	5–12
Galaxies	Mean age	—	4.3	—	—	—	—
Elliptical galaxies	Stellar evolution (mean age)	10–16	10–16	2.5–2.9	6.1–7.5	6.5–8.0	5.5–7.0
Uranium 25% prompt	Time of first formation	11.1	11.1	11.1	11.1	11.1	11.1
"50%"	Time of first formation	7.5	7.5	7.5	7.5	7.5	7.5
Universe	Hubble (galactic expansion)	13.0	13.0	13.0	13.0	13.0	15.0
Universe (flat)	Based on Hubble age	8.6	8.6	8.6	8.3	8.3	—
Universe (closed)	Based on Hubble age	<8.6	—	—	—	—	8.0
Universe (open)	Based on Hubble age	<13 >8.6	—	—	—	—	—

be expected. It may be that the correct explanation of all the discrepancies is poor numbers. However, the discrepancies are so great as to be a source of worry. Perhaps the Hubble age should be the first number to suspect, as it depends on certain statistical assumptions which could conceivably be wrong. However, this would not eliminate the difficulties. A glance at the third column of Table III shows that all the serious discordances are due to one thing, the great age of the globular clusters, old galactic clusters, and Wilson stars (see Table I). Here, however, one should be on fairly firm ground, computing with laws of physics assumed known. As integrations are made with more care and completeness it would be hoped that the theory of stellar evolution should become increasingly sound. It might be fair to say that the present values of the ages of globular clusters are almost surely inaccurate, probably by as much as 30 per cent, but that it is a bit difficult to believe that they could be off by a factor of 3.

It is only old stars whose ages should be corrected. If all stellar ages were corrected by the same percentage, the discrepancy between globular cluster ages and the galactic evolutionary age would remain. This latter age is dependent upon the stellar evolutionary age of young stars for its time scale.

One way in which a discrepancy could appear in the ages of old stars would be for there to be a steady mass loss in all stars. A larger mass in the early phases of a star would increase its evolutionary rate. The rate of mass loss by all stars of a particular mass would need to be quite accurately the same or else there would develop a large spread in the horizontal parts of the giant branch in the Hertzsprung–Russell diagram.

There are several things which argue against this possibility. First, the present mass loss rate by the sun is at least two orders of magnitude too small.[31] Second, the large velocity required for mass ejection from a star on the main sequence demands some violent process, probably employing a magnetic field.[32] It is very difficult to see why different stars with different angular momenta and different magnetic field strengths should eject mass at the same rate.

Another possible explanation requires a cosmology with a time varying gravitational constant. If the gravitational constant is time dependent, from equation (9) the stellar evolutionary time scale t^* is given by

$$t^* = \int_0^t \left(\frac{G}{G_0}\right)^7 dt,\tag{23}$$

where t is ordinary physical time and G_0 is the value of the gravitational constant now. Here a star with a true age of Δt would appear to have an age (evolutionary) of Δt^* and

$$\Delta t^* = \int_{T-\Delta t}^T \left(\frac{G}{G_0}\right)^7 dt,\tag{24}$$

where T is physical time now (the age of the universe). In Table III the evolutionary ages Δt^* are those in column 3, rows 1–3 and 6, whereas the "true" age is tabulated for the two different cosmologies with time varying G in columns 5–8. The space is flat, or substantially flat, for the three cases, columns 5–7. For these examples, G varies with time as a simple power. With the assumption that

$$G(t) = G_0(T/t)^n\tag{25}$$

one obtains

$$\Delta t^* = \frac{T}{7n-1}\left[\left(\frac{T}{T-\Delta t}\right)^{7n-1} - 1\right].\tag{26}$$

For Dirac cosmology $n = 1$. For the Brans–Dicke cosmology,[8] $n = 2/(4 + 3\omega)$. In columns 5–7, Δt is tabulated in the appropriate rows (1, 2, 3, and 7) for the Δt^* appearing in column 3. In column 8 Δt tabulated for an example of a closed space requiring a numerical integration. The radius of the model is so chosen that at the present time it is equal to the Hubble radius. It should be remarked that the Hubble age is assumed to be everywhere 13×10^9 years except in the last column.

It should be noted that for the two cosmologies with time varying gravitation, the ages of globular clusters are reduced drastically. For Dirac's cosmology the reduction is so drastic that the Hubble age would need to be increased by a factor of 3 before a concordance in the age pattern could be obtained.

The three integrations from the Brans–Dicke cosmology which are tabulated, give a reasonably consistent account of the ages. The first one, column 6, gives an age difference between the globular clusters and NGC 188 which is uncomfortably small considering the difference in the heavy element abundance.

Comparing the 7th and 8th columns, it is apparent that the effect on the age pattern of going from a flat space to a closed space can be relatively minor. In order to move the age of the universe to a value consistent with the uranium dating, it is necessary to assume a slightly greater Hubble age for the closed universe, 15.0×10^9 years in comparison with 13.0×10^9 years. After this change the age pattern is concordant.

It might be asked whether there would be other important effects of a larger value of G which might be observed in distant galaxies. Equation (11) shows that the equation for the stellar main sequence is insensitive to the value of G. Thus the increased luminosity of a star on the main sequence due to an increased value of G could equally well be interpreted as due to increased stellar mass. While there should be an effect of a larger G on the luminosity function of a distant galaxy, with blue giants being fewer, brighter, and hotter, and red dwarf stars brighter and hotter than they would be with a constant G, it is unlikely that this effect could be separated from the normal effects of galactic evolution resulting from gas depletion. Things are particularly discouraging if one remembers that even these presumably larger effects have not yet been observed.

Summary and Conclusion

The following stellar evolutionary ages have been discussed; globular clusters, old galactic clusters, stars dated by Wilson, the sun, and elliptical galaxies. Also discussed were the evolutionary age of the galaxy from hydrogen gas depletion, the radioactivity age for the sun and for heavy elements (from the decay of uranium), and the evolutionary ages of the universe from the Hubble expansion age. It was shown that the various ages are in bad disagreement, that none of the standard cosmologies are supported by the data, but that the theory of Brans and Dicke brings all ages into agreement.

On the other hand, an alternative solution is to assume an error of a factor of 2–3 in the computed ages of old stars. While an error this large seems unlikely, the calculations are difficult and the history of these numbers does not inspire great confidence in their present validity.

We conclude that the data discussed are not yet sufficient to support strongly the Brans–Dicke theory. However, the theory provides the only physical explanation for the age discordances that has so far appeared. While it can be argued with good reason that the stellar evolutionary ages of old stars may be wrong, it has yet to be demonstrated how they are wrong. Clearly what is needed is more solid progress on the theory of stellar interiors. It seems certain that progress will come and that compelling evidence for or against the Brans–Dicke theory is not many years off.

Acknowledgments

The author wishes to thank his colleagues in the Princeton Department of Astronomy for introducing him to the mysteries of astronomy. A special thanks is due to G. Field for reading the manuscript and to L. Spitzer for help on the problem of gas turbulence in the galaxy. Finally the author is particularly grateful to M. Schwarzschild for many conversations on problems of stellar evolution. It should be remarked also, that independent of the author's interests in a variable gravitational constant, M. Schwarzschild has considered these questions as they relate to Dirac's theory. Thanks are due also to the members of the authors' research group, particularly to P. Roll and D. Curott for the machine integrations of the cosmological equations of the Brans–Dicke theory.

References and Notes to Appendix 10

[1] L. D. Landau, in *Niels Bohr and the Development of Physics*, edited by W. Pauli (McGraw-Hill Book Company, Inc., New York, 1955).

[2] J. A. Wheeler, Neutrinos, Gravitation and Geometry, Rend. S.I.F. **VI**, 67 (1960).

[3] See the excellent summary by L. Goldberg and E. R. Dyer in Chap. 18, *Science in Space*, edited by L. Berkner and H. Odishaw, (McGraw-Hill Book Company, Inc., New York, 1961).

[4] H. Bondi and T. Gold, *Monthly Notices Roy. Astron. Soc.* **108**, 252 (1948).

[5] F. Hoyle, *Monthly Notices Roy. Astron. Soc.*, **108**, 372 (1948).

[6] Any standard work on relativity such as R. C. Tolman, *Relativity, Thermodynamics, and Cosmology*, (Oxford University Press, New York, 1934).

[7] P. A. M. Dirac, *Proc. Roy. Soc. (London)*, **A165**, 199 (1938).

[8] C. Brans and R. H. Dicke, *Phys. Rev.*, **124**, 925 (1961) (see appendix 7).

[9] H. Bondi, *Cosmology* (Cambridge University Press, New York, 1960), 2nd ed.

[10] The discussion in this section is based on the excellent moongraph by M. Schwarzschild, *Structure and Evolution of the Stars* (Princeton University Press, Princeton, New Jersey (1958).

[11] A. Blaauw, *Stellar Populations* (North-Holland Publishing Company, Amsterdam, 1958), p. 105.

[12] M. Schwarzschild (private communication).

[13] O. C. Wilson, *Astrophys. J.*, **130**, 496 (1959).

[14] J. B. Oke, *Astrophys. J.*, **130**, 487 (1959).

[15] Reports of these great ages have appeared in newspapers and have been widely discussed by astronomers. A proper technical paper has not yet appeared but is expected soon.

[16] J. H. Oort, *Stellar Populations*, p. 415 (see reference 11).

[17] L. Spitzer and M. Schwarzschild, *Astrophys. J.*, **118**, 106 (1953).

[18] L. Spitzer, *Stars and Stellar Systems* (University of Chicago Press, Chicago, Illinois) (to be published), Vol. 7, Chap. 9.

[19] M. Schwarzschild, *Stellar Populations*, p. 207 (see reference 11). Recently these heavy element abundances have been questioned and the indication is that the run of percentages 0.003, 0.020, 0.03, 0.035, 0.04 may be more nearly correct than those given in Table II. If this should be substantiated, one might be forced ultimately to conclude that the massive population II stars

formed at the beginning were more efficient generators, or distributors, of heavy elements than the massive population I stars being formed now. For example, it may be true that type I supernovas are associated with a low metal content of the star, and that in the early days large numbers of massive population II stars ended their days as type I supernovas.

[20] E. E. Salpeter, *Astrophys. J.*, **129**, 608 (1961).

[21] M. Schmidt, *Astrophys. J.*, **129**, 243 (1959).

[22] J. H. Oort, *Stellar Populations*, p. 25 (see reference 11).

[23] J. H. Oort and L. Spitzer, *Astrophys. J.*, **121**, 6 (1955).

[24] A. Sandage, *Stellar Populations*, p. 75 (see reference 11).

[25] E. M. Burbidge, G. R. Burbidge, W. A. Fowler, and F. Hoyle, *Revs. Modern Phys.*, **29**, 547 (1957).

[26] Wm. A. Fowler and F. Hoyle, *Ann. Phys.*, **10**, 280 (1960).

[27] A. Sandage, *Astrophys. J.*, **127**, 513 (1958).

[28] J. Crampin and F. Hoyle, *Monthly Notices Roy. Astron. Soc.*, **122**, 27 (1961).

[29] T. Gold, *Bull. Am. Phys. Soc.*, **6**, 33, (1961).

[30] G. Field (private communication).

[31] C. M. de Turkville, *Nature*, **190**, 156 (1961).

[32] E. N. Parker, *Science in Space*, Chap. 12 (see reference 3).

Appendix II

Dating the Galaxy by Uranium Decay

R. H. Dicke

Reprinted from *Nature*, Vol. 194, No. 4826, pp. 329–330, April 28, 1962

Arp[1] has recently discussed the metal content of stars in clusters of various ages. One striking thing about Arp's data is the indication that the heavy elements were generated primarily by early stars in the halo population. He finds that the very old galactic cluster NGC 188 (16×10^9 years old) has approximately the same heavy element content in its envelope as does the Sun. While there is an indication of slightly more heavy element in very young clusters than in NGC 188, the increase is small (~ 30 per ‑cent) and it may not be statistically significant. While the data are not so firm as to make this conclusion certain, I propose to assume here that the heavy elements were formed primarily by the halo population.

There existed in the early halo population a type of star no longer present in the Galaxy, the massive Population II star. This star may have been supernova prone; it may have been the chief source of the heavy elements.

There appears to be no systematic variation, from one cluster to another, in the ratios of the heavy element abundances. This suggests that uranium was produced at the same time as the other elements, and that Arp's data can be assumed to apply also to the production of uranium.

With this assumption it is easy to obtain an age for the Galaxy based on the radioactive decay of uranium-235. The technique is similar to that first used by Fowler and Hoyle.[2] However, the end result differs by a factor of 2. The production ratio (uranium-235/uranium-238 = 1.64) obtained by Burbidge, Burbidge Fowler, and Hoyle[3] is used. To show how uncritical this assumed production ratio is, ages are calculated also with assumed ratios of 2.0 and 1.0.

Designating by N the fractional abundance of uranium-235 (or uranium-238), that is, the number of atoms of uranium in the interstellar medium per atom of the interstellar medium, N satisfies the differential equation:

$$\frac{dN}{dt} + \gamma N = S(t) \tag{1}$$

Here γ is the decay constant ($\gamma_{235} = 0.97 \times 10^{-9}$ years^{-1}; $\gamma_{238} = 1.54 \times 10^{-10}$ years^{-1}), and S is the fractional production-rate of the isotope ($S_{235}/S_{238} = 1.64$).[3]

Possible production distribution curves are plotted in Fig. 1 against time expressed in units of the present age of the Galaxy (T). Curve (1) is determined by the requirement that the heavy elements be generated prior to the time of formation of NGC 188 ($t = 0.4T$).

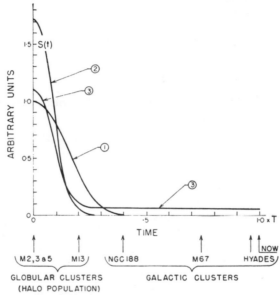

Fig. 1. Uranium production-rate (arbitrary units). T represents the present age of the Galaxy.

This relative time of formation of NGC 188 and the other clusters plotted in Fig. 1 is based on the stellar evolution time-scale which is here being questioned. There is considerable uncertainty about the linearity of the stellar evolutionary time-scale, first because of uncertainties in the evolutionary theory, particularly of Population II stars, secondly because of a possible secular decrease of the gravitational constant, a variation which, if it occurred, would serve to stretch substantially the time-scale for older stars, making an old star appear much older than it actually is.[4-7]

If Salpeter's model[8] of stellar evolution is used, stars being produced at a rate proportional to the amount of gas present in the interstellar medium, it is found that the duration of the halo-forming period is about 0.2T. There is an indication from the very large velocity dispersion in the halo population that even this short period is too long. It is generally agreed that these stellar velocities are fossil remains of the initial high turbulence velocities in the primordial gas of the Galaxy, the stars continuing to move with the original velocities of the gas out of which they were formed. The relaxation-time for this early turbulence to die out was probably less than 2×10^8 years (ref. 9). If the turbulence was maintained for a longer period by radiation from massive stars in the initial population, the duration would be limited by the life-time of these stars to less than 10^9 years. These possibilities are mirrored in curve No. 2 of Fig. 1.

If, as is suggested by Arp's data, the heavy elements were not produced completely by the early Population II stars, but are still being produced to some small extent, it would be reasonable to assume, for the fractional production-rate, the function plotted as curve No. 3 in Fig. 1. This curve represents 60 per cent production associated with the function S_2 (curve No. 2), and 40 per cent distributed uniformly from 0 to T. Consistent with Arp's data, this production distribution curve would give an excess of heavy elements in young clusters of roughly 30 per cent. The constant value of the fractional production-rate, after the halo formation period, is consistent with Salpeter's model of galactic evolution. Fowler and Hoyle[2] assumed that Salpeter's model implied that an exponential function should be used for the production-rate. While this is true of the total production-rate, the fractional production-rate is approximately constant with Salpeter's model.

The solution to equation (1) giving $N(T - 4.7)$, the fractional abundance at the time of formation of the solar system, assumed to be 4.7×10^9 years ago, is:

$$N(T - 4.7) = \int_0^{T-4.7} S(t) \exp(t + 4.7 - T) dt \tag{2}$$

For curves 1 and 2, it is convenient to take $(S)t$ to be in the form of a Gauss error curve:

$$S(t) \sim \exp\left[- \delta\left(\frac{t}{T}\right)^2 \right] \tag{3}$$

and for curve No. 3 it is:

$$S(t) \sim 0.4\,\frac{1}{T} + 0.6\,\frac{2}{\sqrt{\pi}}\,\frac{\delta^{1/2}}{T} \exp\left[- \delta\left(\frac{t}{T}\right)^2 \right] \tag{4}$$

For the three curves of Fig. 1, Nos. 1, 2 and 3, δ assumes the values 24, 72 and 72 respectively. The ratio of the two values of N for N_{235} and N_{238} at the time of formation of the solar system, computed from the present observed ratio of 0.0072, is:

$$\frac{N_{235}(T - 4.7)}{N_{238}(T - 4.7)} = 0.34 \tag{5}$$

Equations (2) and (3) or (4) are substituted in equation (5) which is solved for T to determine the present age of the Galaxy. The various results for curves No. 1, 2 and 3, and for the 3 assumed values of the production ratio, are given in Table 1.

Fowler and Hoyle's[2] determination of 15×10^9 years for the age of the Galaxy is based on the decay of thorium-232 as well as uranium-235 and uranium-238. Because of the long mean life of thorium-232 (20.1×10^9 years), an age determination based on this element is quite sensitive to the assumed production ratio

TABLE 1.

Age of Galaxy from Uranium Decay for the three Assumed Fractional
Production-Rates plotted in Fig. 1.

Curve from Fig. 1	Assumed production ratio $^{235}U/^{238}U$		
	1.0	1.65	2.0
No. 1	7.1×10^9 yr.	7.7×10^9 yr.	8.0×10^9 yr.
No. 2	6.6×10^9 yr.	7.2×10^9 yr.	7.50×10^9 yr.
No. 3	—	7.4×10^9 yr.	—

thorium-232/uranium-238 = 1.65 (ref. 3) and to the present abundance ratio, which, because of the difference in chemistry, cannot be determined which precision Fowler and Hoyle take this ratio to be 3.8 ± 0.3.

Instead of using the thorium-232/uranium-238 ratio to help determine the age, the procedure can be reversed and the above determined ages can be used to calculate a production ratio. With an assumed age of the Galaxy of 7.2×10^9 years and a production-rate given by curve No. 2, the assumed present ratio thorium-232/uranium-238 of 3.8 ± 0.3 implies a production ratio thorium-232/uranium-238 of 1.9 ± 0.2. This to be compared with a value calculated from the theory of nucleosynthesis[3] of 1.65 ± 0.15. The agreement is good.

It should be noted that an age of the Galaxy of 7.2×10^9 years is perfectly consistent with an evolutionary universe with a Hubble age of 12×10^9 years. If, as has been suggested, the universe is closed, but with a large radius, its evolutionary age would be but slightly less than $\frac{2}{3} \times 12 \times 10^9 = 8 \times 10^9$ years (assuming zero for the cosmological constant). This is an encouraging result and indicates that finally the Hubble age of the universe may be settling down to something like its final value.

The difference between the age of $7.4 \pm 0.5 \times 10^9$ years determined here, and the age of approximately 15×10^9 years determined earlier by Fowler and Hoyle may be traced to two factors, the different use made of the thorium data and a different assumption about the form of the production curve. These ages also disagree with the present stellar evolution age of 26×10^9 years (ref. 10). A possible reason for this was discussed[7] previously.

This work was supported by research controls with the U.S. Office of Naval Research and the U. S. Atomic Energy Commission.

Notes and References to Appendix 11

[1] H. Arp, *Science*, **134**, 810 (1961).

[2] W. A. Fowler, and F. Hoyle, *Ann. Phys.*, **10**, 280 (1960).

[3] E. M. Burbidge, G. R. Burbidge, W. A. Fowler, and F. Hoyle, *Rev. Mod. Phys.*, **29**, 547 (1957).

[4] P. A. M. Dirac, *Proc. Roy. Soc.*, A **165**, 199 (1938).

[5] P. Jordan, *Schwerkraft und Weltall* (Vieweg and Sohn, Braunschweig, 1955).

[6] C. Brans, and R. H. Dicke, *Phys. Rev.*, **124**, 925 (1961) (see appendix 7).

[7] R. H. Dicke, *Rev. Mod. Phys.*, **34**, 110 (1962) (see appendix 10).

[8] E. E. Salpeter, *Astrophys. J.*, **129**, 608 (1961).

[9] L. Spitzer, *Stars and Stellar Systems*, 7, chap. 9 (Univ. Chicago Press, in the press).

[10] A. R. Sandage, paper at *Symp. on Stellar Evolution*, Univ. La Plata, Argentina (1960).

Appendix 12

Dirac's Cosmology and the Dating of Meteorites

R. H. Dicke

Reprinted from *Nature*, Vol. 183, pp. 170–171, Jan. 17, 1959

It was long ago suggested by Dirac[1] that, from considerations based upon the sizes of the important physical and astrophysical constants, there were reasons for believing that the gravitational constant, when expressed in atomic units, was not a true constant but that it varied inversely with the age of the universe. It has been pointed out that of the other physical constants, only the weak coupling constant would be expected to vary strongly with time, assuming the correctness of the Dirac hypothesis.[2]

It is interesting to note that an argument based upon such a fundamental consideration as Mach's principle has also been used for supporting the idea of a varying gravitational constant[3,4] and hence by implication perhaps also the β-decay constant.

In the absence of a clear theory, the only type of argument which would enable a calculation of the rate of change of the β-coupling constant with time is the argument based upon Dirac's hypothesis. If this is correct, one would expect the rate of β-decay to vary with time as t^{-n} with $\frac{1}{4} < n < \frac{1}{2}$. The reason for the uncertainty is the rather rough meaning that can be given to the order of magnitude of the large dimensionless numbers.[2] On the other hand, the time-scale is here set by the strong interactions, of which the α-decay is an example. Thus, compared with the ages determined by α-decay, a discrepancy should appear in the ages determined by β-decay. Since reference 2 appeared, there has been a new estimate of the age of the universe,[5] based on the Hubble constant, giving a value of about 13×10^9 years. The purpose of this communication is to use this new age to calculate the correspondence between α-and β-decay ages in order to see if the available data on the meteorite ages can be used for excluding the hypothesis of a weak interaction constant varying with time.

If the time-scale determined by α-decay is designated as t and the β-decay time-scale is t_β, then there is the following connexion between the two scales:

$$t_\beta = \frac{1}{1-n}\left[\left(\frac{t}{T}\right)^{1-n} - n\right] T \qquad (1)$$

where $T = 13 \times 10^9$ years is the present age of the universe and the present times and time-rates are adjusted to be equal for the two different time-scales. Note that equation (1) gives:

$$dt_\beta = \left(\frac{t}{T}\right)^{-n} dt \qquad (2)$$

in accordance with the above assumption about the variation in the β-decay rate. Equation (1) is set out in Table 1 for times in the past and for two extreme values of n.

Table 1 should be interpreted in the following way: If a determination of a potassium-40–argon-40 or rubidium-87–strontium-87 age is assumed to be 4.73 × 10⁹ years, then with the assumption that $n = \frac{1}{4}$, the true age, that is, that given by a lead determination, would be 4.50 × 10⁹ years.

TABLE 1

α-decay age $T - t$	β-decay age $T - t_\beta$	
	$n = \frac{1}{4}$	$n = \frac{1}{2}$
0.0 × 10⁹ years	0.00 × 10⁹ years	0.00 × 10⁹ years
0.5	0.50	0.50
1.0	1.01	1.02
1.5	1.51	1.55
2.0	2.04	2.09
2.5	2.57	2.63
3.0	3.10	3.20
3.5	3.63	3.77
4.0	4.18	4.37
4.5	4.73	4.98

Comparisons between β- and α-decay ages have been made for rubidium-87 and uranium and thorium dates by Aldrich, Wetherill, Tilton and Davis.[6] A similar comparison was made for potassium-40 by Wetherill, Wasserburg, Aldrich, Tilton and Hayden.[7] These comparisons were based largely upon measurements made on rocks with ages less than 2.8 × 10⁹ years. While they seem to be very careful measurements, the expected discrepancy for such ages is at best only 5 per cent. It is very unlikely that these comparisons can be used for excluding the effect in question.

It may be noted that for ages as great as those of the meteorites, ~ 4.5 × 10⁹ years, there is a more noticeable discrepancy between α- and β-ages. Thus for the case of the meteorites there may be a better chance to confirm or reject the hypothesis of a varying weak interaction constant. Unfortunately, because of the discordance between lead–lead[8] and uranium–lead[9] ages of meteorites, there is reasonable doubt about the accuracy of the ages based on lead ratios. Also, because of the spread in ages obtained from the potassium-40–argon-40 method,[10,11] there is reason for believing that some argon has been lost. This throws this determination somewhat in doubt. The strontium-87–rubidium-87 determinations[12] are few and may not have the necessary reliability.

It is concluded that there is no present evidence sufficiently reliable to rule out a variation with time in the β-decay rate.

This work was supported by the U. S. Atomic Energy Commission, the Office of Naval Research and the Higgins Scientific Trust Fund.

Notes and References to Appendix 12

[1] P. A. M. Dirac, *Proc. Roy. Soc.*, A, **165,** 199 (1938).
[2] R. H. Dicke, *Rev. Mod. Phys.*, **29,** 355 (1957).
[3] D. W. Sciama, *Mon. Not. Roy. Astro. Soc.*, **113,** 34 (1953).
[4] R. H. Dicke, *J. Wash. Acad. Sci.*, **48,** 2131 (1958); *Science* (in the press).
[5] A. R. Sandage, *Mon. Not. Roy. Astro. Soc.* (1958).
[6] Aldrich, Wetherill, Tilton and Davis, *Phys. Rev.*, **103,** 1045 (1956).
[7] Wetherill, Wasserburg, Aldrich, Tilton and Hayden, *Phys. Rev.*, **102,** 987 (1956).
[8] C. Patterson, *Geochem. Cosm. Acta*, **10,** 230 (1957).
[9] Hamaguchi, Reed and Turkevich, *Geochem. Cosm. Acta*, **12,** 337 (1957).
[10] G. J. Wasserburg, and R. J. Hayden, *Phys. Rev.*, **97,** 86 (1955).
[11] S. J. Thomson, and K. J. Mayne, *Geochem. Cosm. Acta*, **7,** 169 (1955).
[12] V. E. Schumacher, *Z. Naturforsch.*, **11,** 206 (1956).

INDEX